STORYTIME

Character-building Stories for Children

Pacific Press® Publishing Association
Nampa, Idaho
Oshawa, Ontario, Canada
www.pacificpress.com

Designed by Michelle C. Petz
Front cover image © Veer
Back cover image (teacher and students) © 2008 Jupiterimages Corporation

Starfish edition
ISBN 13: 978-0-8163-2282-4
ISBN 10: 0-8163-2282-1

Skateboard edition
ISBN 13: 978-0-8163-2287-9
ISBN 10: 0-8163-2287-2

13 14 15 16 • 6 5 4 3

STORYTIME
STORIES

The Coopersville Secret Society

KINDNESS TO ANIMALS · COURAGE · GOOD JUDGMENT

Michael pounced on his friend the minute he stepped into the yard. "Hi, Jason," he said. "You got my test ready?" Michael's heart was thumping like the big bass drum in the school marching band. This was the day he had been waiting for—the day he might become a member of the Coopersville Secret Society.

The Coopersville Secret Society was a special club, and only the most popular guys in the school were members. A person couldn't just join the Coopersville Secret Society; he had to be invited to join by someone who was already a member. The club did cool things together. They went camping and had a special clubhouse. More than anything, Michael wanted to belong to the club.

His friend, Jason, was a member, and the club had finally asked Michael to join. But first he had to pass a "test" that the members of the club had decided on. If he was successful, he would be a member in good standing.

Jason leaned against the garage wall and grinned at Michael. "Yeah," he answered, "we have your test ready. But let me give you a word of advice. Use your head, Michael. The test isn't as easy as it sounds."

"What do I have to do," Michael wanted to know.

"See that basket?" Jason asked, pointing to a picnic basket swinging from the handlebars of his bike. "We're going to Mrs. Barker's house down the street. You are to catch her cat, Tiger, and put him in the basket. Then take him out to the edge of town on Willow Road and dump him out there."

"Dump the cat?" Michael asked. He thought he had heard wrong.

"Didn't you hear me?" Jason frowned at him. "What did you think you'd dump—the basket? You've heard the saying, 'A cat always finds its way back,' haven't you? Well, we want to prove it one way or the other today."

As Jason and Michael pedaled their bikes down the street to Mrs. Barker's house, Michael felt as if he were having a bad dream. For the last two days he had tried to imagine what tests the guys would think of for him to do. But he hadn't thought of anything like this. He thought maybe they would ask him to climb high up in the tallest tree in town. Or maybe have him do a hundred pushups. That was the sort of thing he was expecting. But to dump a cat out at the edge of town a long way from home?

Outside the neat white fence that enclosed Mrs. Barker's yard, Jason stopped his bike and shoved the basket into Michael's hands. "Go on," he ordered. "You're on your own now."

With dragging feet, Michael crept along behind the tall bushes that shut off the view from anyone in the house. When he reached the last bush, he was still several feet from the small striped kitten. Tiger was curled up in a ball under a big rosebush.

"Here, kitty, kitty!" Michael called softly. In his heart he was hoping the kitten would run away. But Tiger opened his eyes, pricked up his sharp ears, and stared at Michael with eyes as yellow as the roses on the bush over his head. He must have liked what he saw, because he got up, stretched, and began walking across the grass toward Michael.

Michael wiped the sweat from his forehead. His stomach felt sick. This little kitten would never find its way home from Willow Road. Never!

But if he failed his test, the Coopersville Secret Society would ask someone else to join the club. He wouldn't get to go camping with them next summer. He wouldn't get to play in their clubhouse—a big tree house in Jason's backyard. Michael's thoughts raced around and around like the horses on a merry-go-round. He glanced back to where Jason was standing, watching him.

With a quick grab, Michael picked up Tiger and popped him into the basket. "Shame on you," a little voice seemed to say. "That kitten trusted you."

It was terribly still and quiet in the basket. Could Tiger have smothered already? Michael put his ear to the side of the basket and listened. What he heard made him feel even worse. The kitten was purring happily!

"Come on! Hurry up!" Jason urged impatiently.

Michael didn't even answer. Instead, he lifted the lid of the basket and set Tiger gently on the grass. "I'd never have any fun with the club, remembering what I had done to you," he told the kitten quietly. Slowly he walked back along the row of bushes to where Jason stood. What a day this had turned out to be!

"Why did you take the cat out of the basket?" Jason demanded, with a strange smile on his face.

Michael's face turned red with anger. "Because I don't treat animals that way," he shouted. "I don't care if I did fail your old test. I don't want to belong to a club with guys like that in it!"

"Way to go, Michael!" Jason said, slapping him on the back.

And suddenly they were all there. All the members of the Coopersville Secret Society came tumbling out from behind Mrs. Barker's garage where they had been hiding.

"We knew you'd pass the test," they told Michael.

"What's going on?" Michael asked. "I failed the test, didn't I?"

"No! You passed with flying colors," Jason told him. "If you'd taken the kitten out to Willow Road, then you'd have failed! Don't you remember me telling you to be sure to use your head?"

"So, you didn't really want me to dump Tiger?" Michael still couldn't quite understand what was going on.

"Of course not," Jason said. "If you had taken the cat out of the yard, I'd have taken him away from you and told you that you'd failed the test."

Michael smiled slowly into the faces of the guys surrounding him. He felt good. His friends were the kind of guys he had thought they were all along. And he had passed his test. It was going to be great being a member of the Coopersville Secret Society!

THINK ABOUT IT !?!

- Sometimes the right thing to do seems to be the wrong thing. How can we know the difference?
- What is the most difficult decision you've ever had to make?

When God Controlled a Railroad Train

TRUST IN GOD · FAITH

Many years ago an engineer brought his train to a stop at a little village in Massachusetts where the passengers had only five minutes to get off the train and stretch their legs a bit before the train pulled out again.

"The conductor tells me that the train to Bedford leaves the junction ahead fifteen minutes before we get there," said a sad-looking lady on the platform to the engineer. "That is the last train tonight to Bedford, and I'm trying to get home with a very sick child. I have no money for a hotel. I simply *must* reach that train on time and get home tonight."

"It can't be done," replied the engineer.

"Would it be possible for you to hurry a little?" asked the anxious, tearful mother.

"No, Ma'am. I have a schedule, and the rules say I must follow it exactly."

The woman turned away sorrowfully. But a moment later, she was back. "Are you a Christian?" she asked the engineer.

He looked somewhat puzzled. "Yes, I am," he answered. "Why do you ask?"

"Will you pray with me that the Lord may in some way delay that train at the junction?"

"Well . . . Yes, I'll pray with you, but I don't have much faith that the train will be delayed long enough for you to make your connection."

Just then the conductor called out, "All aboard!"

The poor woman hurried to get back into the train and take care of her sick child. The engineer quickly climbed to his spot in the engine, and soon the train was puffing its way down the track, climbing the grade. In her seat on the train, the woman prayed for God to help her to reach the Bedford train in time. Up in his seat at the throttle, the engineer also prayed. "Lord," he said, "delay that Bedford train only ten minutes, and I'll make up the extra five minutes!"

"Somehow," the engineer later recalled, "everything seemed to go according to some plan. After I prayed, I couldn't help increasing my speed just a little! We hardly paused at the first stop. People got on and off more quickly than I've ever seen before. In half a minute, the conductor was waving his lantern, and we were off once more. I began to have more faith that we would reach the junction before that other train left.

"Once over the summit of the mountain, it was easy to give the engine a little more

steam, and then a little more. I prayed, and the train seemed to shoot down the rails like an arrow. I sensed something was pushing us forward, and I couldn't hold her back! We came rushing into the junction six minutes ahead of schedule. And there stood the Bedford train! Its conductor was still standing on the platform, his lantern resting at his side."

Now, these trains never connected with each other. They weren't intended to; the schedule didn't allow for it. No message had been sent ahead to hold the Bedford train. There was no reason it should not have left the station several minutes earlier. Yet, there it stood—waiting.

The conductor of the Bedford train approached the engineer of the train that had just pulled into the junction. "Well," he inquired, "will you tell me what we're waiting for? Somehow I felt that I needed to wait until you arrived at the station tonight. But I don't know why."

"I can tell you," replied the engineer. "I have a woman on board my train who has a sick child and who must get home tonight. She has been praying—and I have been praying—that somehow your train would still be here when we arrived. And here you are!"

Think About It ?!

- Does God know what we need before we tell Him about it in prayer?
- Do you think God ever gets tired of doing good things for us?

Tommy's Monkey

KINDNESS TO ANIMALS · HONESTY

"Hey, mister," shouted Tommy, "you've lost your monkey!" Tommy had found a baby monkey beside the road as the circus was leaving town. He picked it up and began running after the trucks that were slowly beginning to pull onto the road. Now he was almost out of breath.

A man looked down at Tommy from his seat in the circus truck. "I didn't lose that monkey, boy!" he shouted. "The monkey's dying, so I threw it out.

Tommy could hardly believe his ears. How could anyone throw out a poor little monkey because he was dying?

"Can't you take care of him until he's better?" he asked indignantly.

"No. That monkey's no good. He'll die before night. There's no use keeping him."

Tears of anger and pity filled Tommy's eyes. "Well, sir, you'll be sorry someday that you treated him like that!" And with those words, Tommy turned and walked away with the monkey carefully cradled in his arms. The dusty road felt hot to Tommy's bare feet, so when he came to a pond beside the road, he was glad to sit on the bank and put his feet in the water. Then he gave the little monkey a drink.

"Well, monkey," Tommy said, "that circus man may think he knows a lot, but I'm going to do my best to show him that he doesn't know a live monkey when he sees one! I don't know much about doctoring people or monkeys, but my mom knows a lot." So, after pouring some cool water on the monkey's head, the boy put the little bundle of fur inside his shirt and hurried home.

When Tommy arrived, tired and hungry, the monkey was still alive and seemed a little more alert than he had been when Tommy found him.

"It seems to me all he needs is good food and some peace and quiet," said Tommy's mother when she saw the little invalid. "I guess the poor thing is tired of all the noise and bustle of the circus. I'll cook him some oatmeal. You make him a clean bed of straw and put some fresh water in a pan beside it. Then we have to leave him alone. We've done everything we can for him; nature will have to do the rest."

After the monkey had eaten a few bites and had a drink of water, Tommy put him on the straw and left him in the shed in the backyard. It was hard not to keep checking on him, but Tommy knew his mother was right: the tired, sick little animal needed rest more than anything else.

The next morning, as soon as it was light, Tommy got up and ran to see how the monkey was getting along. He hesitated to open the door, afraid of what he might find. Imagine his surprise when looking cautiously around the door, Tommy found the little monkey perched on a rafter above his head!

Tommy was so happy he clapped his hands, and the monkey ran chattering into the farthest corner.

There, thought Tommy regretfully, *the first thing I do is scare him! I guess I don't deserve to have a monkey!* But they were soon good friends again, and Tommy ran to tell his mother the wonderful news that the monkey was much better.

The monkey was still not well by any means, and Tommy and his mother had to nurse him carefully for a whole week before he was cured. Then Tommy was the proudest boy in the whole world. He named the monkey Peter, and the animal followed Tommy everywhere like a dog. He was so intelligent that he seemed to understand everything Tommy said.

"Mother," Tommy said, "I can hardly believe that I have a real live monkey that won't run away from me! Do you remember how I always dreamed of one? But I never thought I'd actually get a monkey of my very own!"

Mother looked serious. "Have you thought, Tommy, of what will happen when the circus comes back to town?"

Tommy's eyes opened wide. "Aw, Mom, you don't mean that Peter will leave me and go back to the circus, do you?"

"No," Mom said. "But the man didn't actually give you the monkey, did he?"

"But he threw him away," Tommy exclaimed. "I figure I have a right to Peter when I saved his life!"

"Well, think it over, Tommy," his mother cautioned. "Think about it."

Tommy did think about it. He thought about it a lot, and finally he decided that Mother was right. He would have to give Peter back to his owner when the circus returned to town. But Tommy thought some more, and he decided at last that there might be a way out of his problem. And with this idea in mind, Tommy began saving his nickels and dimes and quarters. He looked for odd jobs he could do to earn more money. Maybe he could buy Peter from the circus man if he had enough money.

Tommy never knew a year to go by so quickly. And as the time grew near for the circus to come to town again, he grew more and more afraid. He couldn't bear the thought of losing his friend, especially since he had taught Peter to do so many clever tricks.

At last the circus trucks began pulling into town. Men were setting up the big tents in a large field on the edge of town. Tears filled Tommy's eyes as he walked toward all the noise and activity

with Peter perched in his usual spot on his shoulder. "When he sees how smart you are," Peter told his friend, "he'll want you back for sure."

Peter didn't understand the tears, and he chattered excitedly as they drew nearer and nearer the circus tents. "What do you want, boy?" asked a big man who was leading an elephant. He seemed to be the man in charge.

Tommy hesitated. "Well, sir . . . You see, sir . . ." He stopped. Then the story rushed out of him—about how he had rescued the sick little monkey and had nursed him back to health and taught him tricks and how they had become such good friends.

"Yes," the man said. "I heard about that fellow who threw out a monkey that was sick. I fired him. I don't allow such things to happen in my circus if I can help it. So this is the sick little guy, is it? Well, you're a smart boy to nurse him back to life. What are you going to do with him now?"

"He's yours, sir," Tommy said in a choked voice. "The man didn't really give him to me; he just left him, and I took care of him. But he's a really cute monkey, and you'll be nice to him, won't you?" There was such a big lump in Tommy's throat that he had trouble getting the words out.

"Can he do any tricks?" asked the circus man.

"Yes, sir." And Tommy had Peter go through all the tricks he had taught him.

"Wow!" the man exclaimed. "He's a smart little monkey, isn't he? How much do you want for him?"

Tommy gasped. "How much do I want for him?"

It took a moment for Tommy to understand what the man had said. Then the words just tumbled out of his mouth one after the other. "Why, sir! If you think he's mine, just let me keep him. That's all I want. You see, he's my friend, and I couldn't sell my friend. I don't want money. All I want is Peter!" And he buried his face in Peter's soft fur.

The circus man put an arm around Tommy's shoulders. "You're right, Son," he said. "There's not enough money in the world to buy a friend. You keep him. And bring him here to the circus to see his mother and the rest of the circus every day if you want to. No, you won't have to pay to get in. You and Peter will be my guests at the circus all week!"

Think About It ?!

- Do you have a pet? If so, what kind of animal is it? Would you enjoy having a monkey for a pet?
- Have you ever seen someone mistreating an animal? What did they do? How did you feel about it?

The Boy Who Wouldn't Give Up

PERSEVERANCE · DETERMINATION · COURAGE

Many years ago, a man—Judge Pemberton—was in a bookstore in Cincinnati, Ohio, when a boy came into the store. He was about twelve years old and was dressed in worn, shabby clothes. The judge watched him as he came to the counter.

"Do you have any geography books?" the boy asked the owner of the store.

"We have plenty of geography books," the man replied.

"How much do they cost?" the boy asked.

"One dollar."

The boy looked surprised. Putting his hand in his pocket, he pulled out some coins and began counting them. There were several nickels and dimes, but mostly pennies. He counted them three or four times before he put them back in his pocket. At last, he turned to go, saying softly to himself, "I didn't know they cost so much."

He got to the door and then turned back. "I have only sixty-two cents," he told the shopkeeper. "Could you let me have the geography book now and wait a little while until I get the rest of the money?"

He eagerly waited for the answer, and seemed to shrink a little inside his ragged clothes when the shopkeeper kindly told him that he couldn't do that. The boy was plainly disappointed, but he tried to smile and then left the store.

Judge Pemberton left as well, and caught up with the boy on the street.

"Where are you going now," he asked.

"I'll go to another bookstore and try again, sir," the boy replied.

"May I go with you," the judge asked, "and see what happens?"

The boy looked surprised. "Sure," he said. "If you want to."

The answer was the same at the second bookstore—and at two more that the boy visited, as well.

"Are you going to try again?" asked the judge as they left the fourth bookstore.

"Yes, sir," the boy assured him. "I'll try them all. Otherwise, I won't know whether or not I can get a geography book."

As the judge and the boy entered the fifth bookstore, the boy walked up to the counter and told the owner just what he wanted and how much money he had.

"You want this book very much, don't you?" the man asked.

"Yes, sir. Very much."

"Why do you want a geography book so badly?"

"To study it, sir. You see, I can't go to school; I have to work most days to help my mother. My father is dead. He was a sailor, and I want to know about the places that he used to go."

"I see," said the bookstore owner softly.

"I'm going to be a sailor too, when I grow up," the boy told him.

"Is that right?" the man replied. "Well, I tell you what I will do. I will let you have a new geography book, and you can pay me the rest of

the money when you can. Or I can let you have a used geography book for fifty cents."

"Are all the pages in the used book?" the boy asked. "The very same pages as the new book—only used?"

"Yes," the man answered. "It's just exactly like the new book, except that it isn't new."

"Then I'll take the used book," the boy said. "And I'll have twelve cents left. I'm glad they didn't let me have a book at any of the other stores."

The bookstore owner looked up puzzled when the boy said this. And Judge Pemberton explained that this was the fifth store the boy had come to looking for a geography book. The owner seemed impressed. When he handed the boy the book, he also handed him a new pencil and a tablet of paper.

"Here's a little gift," he said, "because you're so determined to learn. Always have perseverance and courage, and you'll do all right in life."

"Thank you, sir," said the boy. "You're very kind."

"What's your name?" the man asked.

"William Haverly, sir."

The judge looked at William. "You like books very much, don't you?"

"Indeed, I do." And the judge saw his eyes sweep longingly across the shelves of books in the store.

"Well, William," said the judge, "Here are twenty dollars. Twenty dollars will buy some books for you."

Tears of joy came into the boy's eyes. "Can I buy anything I want with it?" he asked.

"Yes, you can buy anything you want with the money."

"Then I'll buy a book for my mother," the boy said. "And another book for myself. I thank you very much, and I hope some day I can pay you back." The judge left him standing in the bookstore with

a great smile on his face.

Many years later the judge went to Europe on one of the finest sailing ships then making the voyage across the Atlantic. The weather was beautiful until the very last few days before reaching port. Then a terrific storm arose. It was so violent that it would have sunk the ship if it had not been for the heroic efforts of the captain. The ship sprung a leak that threatened to fill the ship and sink it.

The crew were all strong men, and the officers were experienced and capable. But after they had manned the pumps for an entire night, the water was still gaining on them. They gave up in despair

and were getting the life boats ready, although they knew that the chances were slim that such small boats could survive in the violent sea.

The captain had been in his cabin with his charts, trying to figure how far it was to land. Now he came on deck. When he understood the situation, he ordered the seamen back to the pumps. At his command they turned to their task once more. Then the captain started to go below to examine the leak. As he passed, the judge asked him, "Captain, is there any hope?" Several other passengers nearby came close to hear his reply.

The captain looked at the judge and said, "Yes, sir. There is hope as long as one inch of this boat remains above water! When I see none of the ship above water I will abandon the vessel, and not before—nor shall one of my crew. I will do everything humanly possible to save it, and if we fail, it won't be because we didn't try. Come, every man of you, and help work the pumps!"

The captain's courage and perseverance and powerful will captured every mind on that ship, and everyone went to work. "I'll land you safely at the dock in Liverpool," the captain assured us, "if only you will each do your part."

And he did land the passengers and crew safely, but the ship sank as they were mooring it to the dock. The captain stood on the deck of the sinking ship as the passengers filed down the gangplank. The judge was the last to leave. As he passed, the captain took him by the hand, "Judge Pemberton," he said, "you don't recognize me, do you?"

"I don't recall that we have ever met before," the judge answered.

"Oh, but we have," said the captain. "Years ago in Cincinnati. Do you remember the boy who was looking for a geography book?"

"And are you that boy?" the judge exclaimed.

"Yes, I'm William Haverly. God bless you for what you did for me back then."

"And God bless you, Captain, for your perseverance and courage," the judge replied.

Think About It!?!

- What do you think the boy in this story would have done if he hadn't been able to get a geography book at the last store he visited? Would he have given up?
- Have you ever wanted something as badly as he wanted the book? Did you get it?

How Polly Cured the Cat

GETTING ALONG WITH OTHERS · RESOURCEFULNESS

Did I ever tell you how our cat, Skunker, was cured of the habit of catching birds? No? Well, I must tell you, because it was a great lesson for Skunker—a lesson he wasn't expecting at all.

Skunker was a good pet. He loved to be rubbed, and he had learned to do some tricks. But he had one big fault, which was a really bad fault—no bird was safe if Skunker was around.

He had already eaten two of Mother's canaries, and the neighbors had threatened to have him taken away to the animal shelter in town if he ever came into their yards to hunt the birds there. But last, however, Skunker met his equal. Here is how it happened.

Aunt Clara wrote to Mother that she would spend the summer with us and would bring her big parrot—which she said was a macaw. Now, Mother was perfectly willing to have Aunt Clara stay with us and for her to bring her parrot. We children were delighted too; we liked Aunt Clara, and we had never been around a parrot before. Neither had Skunker, as you will see!

One day Mother was busy getting Aunt Clara's room ready, and John and I were helping her. Suddenly Mother stopped what she was doing. "Oh, dear!" she said. "I forgot about Skunker. I'm happy that Aunt Clara is coming to stay with us for a while, but I forgot how much Skunker likes birds. What if anything should happen to Aunt Clara's parrot?"

So, we decided to give Skunker away. Now let me tell you something you may not know. It is easy to give a cat away, but once you give him away, he may not stay given! We gave Skunker to a man who grew vegetables on a farm four miles outside of town. We thought Skunker would be happy there, and Mother felt much better about Aunt Clara bringing her parrot when she came to stay with us.

Aunt Clara came with trunks and suitcases and a big cage containing Polly, her pet parrot. Polly was a very large, beautiful bird—her feathers were green and gold and red, and she had a wise solemn expression and a quick tongue. She must have been tired after her long journey, because she said, "Polly's sleepy! Good night! Hello boys!" And she stretched her neck and legs to get rested.

We would have liked to listen to her talk all night, but Aunt Clara said that if we kept Polly awake too long, she would be cross in the morning. So, John carried her cage to Aunt Clara's room. The next morning we heard cries and squawks and whistles coming from Aunt Clara's room that startled us at first—until we remembered Polly. Soon we heard a sound like laughter and Polly saying, "Ha, ha, boys! Good morning! Hello boys!"

While we were eating breakfast that first morning, we could hear Polly squawking and jabbering upstairs. Aunt Clara told us that she had put Polly's cage on the window sill so she could get some fresh air and sunshine. "I saw a big, gray cat outside in the backyard," Aunt Clara said. "Polly could see it too, and that's why she is making so much noise."

We all looked at each other. "A big, gray cat . . . ?" It sounded like Skunker, but we knew it couldn't be. Skunker was four miles outside of town living with the man who sold vegetables.

After breakfast, John was allowed to bring the cage down to the dining room, and there is where Polly stayed the whole time Aunt Clara was visiting us. When John set the cage down, Aunt Clara opened the cage door, and Polly came out with a slow step. She looked at us and said, "Polly wants a bath! Polly wants her breakfast! Hello boys!" We couldn't help but laugh at her, which seemed to please her very much. She sat near her cage holding a bit of bread in her claw. All at once, she stretched her neck, dropped the bread, and called out, "Cat! Cat! Hello boys!" At the same time, she was looking intently at something that had appeared at the window.

That something was Skunker! He had come home again! We were worried, of course. We knew how much Skunker liked to hunt and eat birds. Aunt Clara didn't look worried at all. She said quietly, "You don't have to be afraid for Polly. She's a match for any cat I ever saw." So, then we thought that it might be fun to see what the cat would do, for we knew that Skunker was no coward. But he only looked at the bird this time and sprang out of the window when Polly screamed at him, "Goodbye, cat! Who's afraid? Who's afraid?"

For two or three days Skunker didn't try to come into the house, much less the dining room where Polly had taken up residence. After awhile, even Mother began to lose her fears for Polly's safety. Then Skunker began to sit quietly near a window or an open door to the dining room. He looked at Polly with longing eyes, but he was ready to run at a moment's notice if need be. It seemed that the cat was astonished that the bird was able to talk. But finally, he thought (I suppose) that she was only a bird after all, and he began longing for a meal that he had captured himself.

You can guess what happened. One day we heard a great commotion in the dining room. Mother came running with a terrified look on her face. We children hurried to the sound of the battle, eager to see what was happening. In a minute, here came Aunt Clara, as well.

We had never seen such a sight as we saw in the dining room when we got there. Everyone stood spellbound for a moment and then burst out laughing. Evidently, Polly had been taking a nap on the window sill when Skunker decided to attack. When we arrived, Polly was holding the cat in her strong claws and had his ear clamped in her powerful beak. Skunker was howling and hissing and spitting and trying his best to use his claws against the bird. But there seemed little chance of that.

The whole time, Polly kept making a funny little noise down deep in her throat. Then, as we watched, parrot and cat rolled off the window sill and onto the floor. For a second, there was a wild blur of fur and feathers. Then Skunker dashed madly past us and out the door. We could hear him spitting even after he reached the backyard.

Polly picked herself up off the floor and began to smooth her ruffled feathers. Evidently, she was no worse for her tussle with the cat. But she was still very angry. She screamed after Skunker, "Cat! Cat! Polly's mad! Hello boys!"

She would hardly let Aunt Clara soothe her, and for two or three days she was irritable and quarrelsome. No one dared to say "Cat!" in Polly's hearing.

Needless to say, Skunker was cured of his habit of hunting birds. A few days later, he came back home with a torn ear, but nothing could persuade him to go into the dining room. If he even heard Polly's voice, he would put back his ears and slink away as quickly as he could!

Think About It

- Why do some animals—like cats and birds or cats and dogs—usually not get along happily together?
- Do you play happily with your friends or are you always getting into arguments? Why?

CHAPTER 6

THE TALKING SAW

TRUTHFULNESS · DEPENDABILITY

Sam was using his favorite tool. As he pushed the saw back and forth, he watched the teeth bite evenly into the board.

Sam and Joe were building a birdhouse. Sam's dad had helped them draw the plans and had told the boys they could use his tools to build it.

"Where can we put the birdhouse when we've finished it?" Sam asked.

"We could put it on that pine tree next to the garage," Joe suggested.

Just then Sam's mother called, "Dinner's ready, Sam!"

Sam straightened up with his hand on the saw. "We'll have to stop now and put the tools away," he said. "I promised Dad I'd be careful with his tools and put them back where they belong."

"Leave the saw," Joe said, "and I'll finish cutting that board. I'll put the saw away when I'm through. I have to go home too."

"All right," Sam replied. And he left Joe to complete the work on the board and put the saw away.

After dinner, Sam did his homework and got ready for bed. Just as he was brushing his teeth, it began to rain outside. It was only a sprinkle of rain, but Sam thought about the saw. *Joe said he would put it away,* he thought to himself. *Surely he did.* Joe was Sam's best friend, but Sam knew that Joe didn't always follow through and do what he said he would do. He almost went out to the garage to make sure the saw was safely in its place, but it was late. And after all, Joe *had* said he would take care of it.

The next morning Sam went out the back door on his way to school. To his surprise, there lay the saw on the back step right where he and Joe had been working the evening before. *I should have known I couldn't depend on Joe to put it away,* Sam thought. He was angry with Joe, but he also felt it was somewhat his fault as well because he hadn't put the saw away carefully himself. After all, he had promised Dad to take good care of his tools. Sam picked the saw up and looked at it closely. It was dry and seemed to be all right.

I'll put it away now, and Dad won't ever know it stayed out all night, he thought to himself.

After school that afternoon Sam and Joe were busy

once more working on the birdhouse they were building. They nailed the pieces of wood together, and then they painted the birdhouse a bright blue. When the paint was dry, Sam's father came out to see their work.

"Can we put it on the pine tree next to the garage?" asked Sam.

"OK," Dad said. "Let's see how it looks there." He held the birdhouse up against the trunk of the pine tree.

"That looks fine," Joe said.

"But it needs to go just a little higher—right where that small branch is growing," Sam said. "We can cut off that branch and then nail the birdhouse to the tree right there."

"I'll cut it off," Sam's dad offered, and he went into the garage to get his saw. In a moment he was back. His face was frowning as he looked at the saw in his hand. "I thought you boys were going to take good care of my tools," he said.

Sam looked at Joe, and Joe looked at Sam. Then they both looked at the ground. Neither boy said a word.

Finally, Sam said, "The saw was left out overnight. There was a little rain, but the saw was dry this morning. I didn't think it was hurt, so I didn't tell you. Who *did* tell you, Dad?"

His father held up the saw so that Sam and Joe could see it. There were tiny dots of red rust all over the blade. "The saw told me," Dad said. "I can clean it and oil it, and it will be OK. But just remember: When you do something you shouldn't have done, it's always better to admit it and not try to cover it up. Now, let's get that birdhouse fastened to the tree!"

THINK ABOUT IT ?!

- Can people depend on you to do what you say you will do?
- Who do you think was more to blame for not taking care of the saw—Sam or Joe? Why?

CARL AND GROVER

TRUST IN GOD · GENEROSITY · FRIENDSHIP

Carl was trying hard not to cry. After all, he was almost nine years old, and he knew nine-year-old boys didn't cry. But he felt like crying. He buried his face in Grover's soft brown fur and felt better. Grover was his very best friend. Grover didn't care that Carl couldn't run and play like the other boys and girls at school. When Carl went tap, tap, tapping down the street with his crutches, Grover didn't seem to mind at all. He would follow close behind or sometimes he would run ahead as fast as his four feet would carry him—and then come racing back to Carl.

And now Carl didn't know what he was going to do, because Grover had to have a license, and the license cost $12.50 and Carl didn't have $12.50. Carl didn't have even fifty cents.

The animal control officer had told Carl that a new rule passed by the city council required all dogs to be registered and have a license. The license would be a small metal tag that would be fastened to a collar around the dog's neck. If Grover didn't have a license by

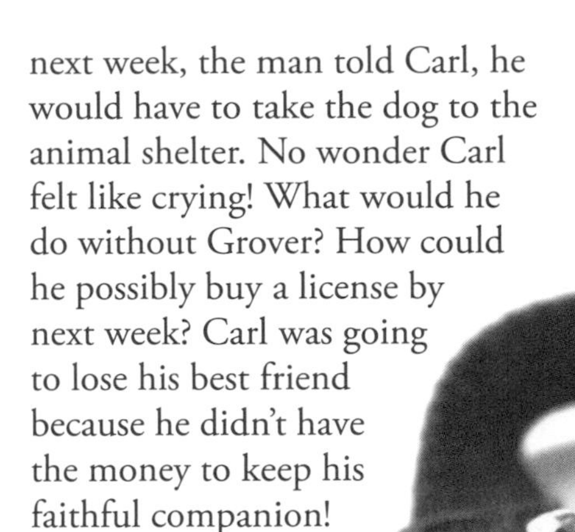

next week, the man told Carl, he would have to take the dog to the animal shelter. No wonder Carl felt like crying! What would he do without Grover? How could he possibly buy a license by next week? Carl was going to lose his best friend because he didn't have the money to keep his faithful companion!

Just then Carl remembered something he had heard his pastor say in church. The pastor had said that Jesus always hears our prayers. He had said that if boys and girls will pray to Jesus, He will hear and answer their prayers.

"That's what I'll do," Carl said out loud. "I'll pray and ask Jesus to let me keep Grover."

After he had whispered a prayer, Carl felt better. He looked up and saw Tommy coming down the street.

Now Grover was Carl's very best friend, but Tommy was his very best human friend. Carl felt so much better after his short prayer to Jesus that he even smiled when he saw Tommy coming toward him—especially when he saw the big grin on Tommy's face. It was clear that Tommy was a very, very happy boy.

"Why are you so happy?" Carl asked.

"I'm on my way to Mason's Hardware Store," Tommy told him. "I'm going to look at the new bicycle in the window one more time. It's really a great bike. I've been saving and saving my money to buy it. I almost have enough. I think I'll have enough money next week to buy it!"

Carl was happy for his friend. He couldn't ride a bicycle himself, of course, since he had to walk with crutches. But he could imagine how much fun it would be.

Tommy sat down on the grass beside Carl and began to rub Grover's head. Grover rolled over and wagged his tail. Carl told Tommy about Grover needing a license and how he had prayed to Jesus to help him. "Jesus is going to let me keep Grover," he said. "I know he is."

A few minutes later, Tommy got up and was on his way to the hardware store. But as he walked down the street, he kept thinking about Grover and Carl. *He sure doesn't have much to make him happy,* Tommy thought to himself. *It would break his heart to have to give up Grover.*

Just then he arrived at the window where the precious bicycle stood. It was great just to look at it and think about flying down the street

holding on to the handlebars! But then, a picture of Grover and Carl filled Tommy's mind. He sighed, *Someone has to buy that license,* he thought to himself. *Besides, it would be fun to help Jesus answer Carl's prayer.* He stood in front of the window thinking very hard. At last Tommy made a decision. *The bicycle will just have to wait a little longer,* he thought.

Running back to where he had left Carl a few minutes before, Tommy asked, "Carl, could Grover stay at my house just for tonight? Can I borrow him? I don't have a dog, and it would be fun to keep Grover for a little while."

Carl tightened his arms around his faithful friend. He wasn't sure he wanted Grover staying overnight at Tommy's house. "Won't your mother mind?" he asked.

"She won't mind," Tommy assured him.

"Do you promise to take good care of him?" Carl asked. "You won't forget to feed him or make sure he has lots of water to drink?"

"Of course, I'll take good care of him," Tommy insisted.

"OK," Carl agreed. "If you're sure you'll take good care of him. But only for tonight."

The next morning Carl sat on the top step of his back porch watching the neighborhood children play. He missed Grover, and he hoped Tommy would bring him back soon. He knew Jesus was going to answer his prayer. He had faith.

Then all at once Grover came bounding around the corner of the house. With a hop and jump, the excited dog was in his master's arms. "Grover!" Carl exclaimed as his friend licked his face and wriggled happily. Then, as Carl was rubbing Grover's fur, he felt something around the dog's neck. It was a brand new collar! Carl looked at it carefully. Attached to the collar was a small metal disc—the license that the city required!

Carl let out a happy shout! Jesus had answered his prayer! "Thank You, Jesus," he prayed.

A few blocks away, Tommy was sitting on his bedroom floor counting quarters and nickels and dimes. Beside him, turned upside down, was the jar he had been keeping his money in for weeks as he saved for the shiny bicycle in the window of Mason's hardware store. *I'll just have to keep saving a little longer,* Tommy thought to himself as he finished counting the coins. *But I'm glad I helped Jesus answer Carl's prayer. It was fun buying Grover's license and collar—almost as much fun as it will be to ride my new bicycle.* And he poured all the quarters and nickels and dimes back into his jar and put it in the far corner of his closet.

THINK ABOUT IT ?!

- Have you ever prayed, asking Jesus for something? Did He answer your prayer?
- Suppose the new bicycle was sold before Tommy could finish saving enough money to buy it. Do you think he would be sorry he helped his friend? Why or why not?

Beth and Betty

CHEERFULNESS · HELPFULNESS

Once upon a time there was a little girl named Beth who had two faces! One face was a very pretty, smiling face. Beth wore this face only when there were visitors in her house or around strangers. Her other face—a frowning, unhappy face—she put on whenever she was around her family, the people who loved her best and who did the most for her.

When her Aunt Margaret came for a long visit, everyone hoped Beth would be wearing her pretty face all the time. And she did for several days. Aunt Margaret brought her camera with her and took several pictures of Beth with her pretty smile. But after a few days, Aunt Margaret became just like a regular member of the household, and then she learned about Beth's other face.

One day Beth was in her room playing when Mother called. "Beth, would you please come and help me set the table for dinner? Will you?"

"I just hate to set the table," complained the angry little girl in her angriest tone of voice. She threw down the game she was playing and came into the kitchen where her mother and Aunt Margaret were getting dinner ready. Beth was wearing her other face—the frowning, unhappy face. She didn't see her aunt pick up her camera. There was a soft "click," but Beth didn't hear it. She was too busy slamming drawers and scattering the silverware as she unhappily began to set the table as her Mother had asked.

The next morning Beth came down to breakfast after everyone else had finished. She was still wearing her unhappy face. Aunt Margaret was sitting at the breakfast table reading the newspaper. On the table in front of her sat her camera. Mother brought Beth some cereal and orange juice and toast. But nothing seemed to please the little girl. She fussed and complained about everything. In fact, she was so cross and miserable and so busy complaining that she didn't notice at all when her aunt picked up the camera and took a picture or two.

Throughout that day Aunt Margaret took a lot of pictures. All day long she was snapping this picture and then that. She took so many pictures that everyone soon stopped paying attention and went right on with whatever they were doing while Aunt Margaret took their picture.

Late that afternoon Aunt Margaret said, "Beth, would you like to see the pictures I've taken today? I can put them on the computer from my camera, and you can see them on the screen."

"OK," Beth agreed and stood by the computer while her aunt connected the cables to the camera. Soon the images were loaded and began appearing on the screen.

"Oh, look!" Aunt Margaret said, pointing to the picture of Beth she had taken at the breakfast table that morning. "That looks just like you. The last thing your grandmother said to me when I left to come here was, 'Be sure to get some good pictures of Beth.' "

Beth looked at the picture of herself and

wondered if her grandmother really would be happy to see it after all. Then, one by one, her aunt began to scroll through all the pictures she had taken during the day. There were a lot of pictures of Beth, and she was wearing her frowning, unhappy face in nearly every one. She wished she could delete them all, but of course it was her aunt's camera, and she couldn't. She didn't like these pictures at all.

Beth was even more unhappy the next day. Aunt Margaret had printed color copies of the pictures. She had a large color print of the picture of Beth at the breakfast table looking all cross and angry and miserable. "I printed it especially for your grandmother," she told Beth. "She'll probably want to hang it on the wall at home."

"Aunt Margaret, please don't give it to Grandmother," begged Beth. "I don't think it looks nice at all. Here, give her this one." And Beth picked up a picture of herself wearing her happy face—the one she wore when visitors were around.

"We'll give Grandmother both pictures," Aunt Margaret said. "We'll call one *Beth* and the other one we'll call *Betty.* In fact, let's tape them up on the wall here by the computer. You can decide which face you want to stay up. When you're wearing your happy face, we'll put *Beth* on the wall. But when you're wearing your frowning face, we'll take *Beth* down and put up *Betty.* You can decide which picture stays up."

After that, Beth wore her happy face for several days, and her aunt took down *Betty* and left *Beth* on the wall. But habits are hard to break, and one day *Betty* came down to breakfast instead of Beth, so Betty's picture went back up on the wall. That very morning a friend of Mother's stopped by the house. She saw *Betty* on the wall and asked, "Whose picture is that?"

"Oh," Mother replied to her friend, "that is a little girl who comes here quite often. Her name is Betty."

Beth was so embarrassed. She slipped upstairs to her room. Aunt Margaret found her there a little while later, crying as if her heart would break. She sat down beside Beth on the floor and took her hand. "Beth," she asked, "do you know what a hypocrite is?"

Beth shook her head.

"A hypocrite is a person who pretends to be something he or she isn't. You are either Beth or Betty. If you are really and truly like Betty and only pretend

to be like Beth when strangers are around, then you're a hypocrite. And to be a hypocrite is worse than being Betty. Really, though, I believe you are Beth at heart, but you've gotten into the habit of acting like Betty—so much so that it's possible Beth may go away completely and never come back. I think it's time now to send either Beth or Betty away for good, don't you?"

Beth nodded her head.

"Well, which little girl do you want to be?"

"I want to be Beth," she sobbed.

"Good," said her aunt. "That's what I thought. I'm glad to see Betty go, and I'm sure your mother will be too. Now, I'm going to take Betty down off the wall, and if she never comes back, I promise not to show her picture to Grandmother. I will be going back home in a month. That's a long time, and if Betty hasn't come back before I leave, then I think we can count on it that she won't ever come back. And I'll throw away all the pictures of Betty and delete them out of my camera, and we will just forget about her completely."

Now, Betty didn't want to leave, and Beth had to work hard to drive her away with a cheerful smile. But she did. And before Aunt Margaret left, Beth watched her delete all the pictures of Betty from her camera.

"You won't show Grandmother any pictures of Betty, will you?" Beth asked anxiously.

"There aren't any pictures of Betty left to show her," replied Aunt Margaret. "I don't think Betty is ever going to come back again to have her picture taken."

"I don't think so either," Beth said with a smile. "I don't think she is coming back at all!"

Think About It!?!

- Do you have more than one face? Which one do you wear most often?
- Why are habits so difficult to change?

SAVED FROM A PANTHER

TRUST IN GOD, · COURAGE

Near the summit of a mountain in Pennsylvania was a small place called Honeyville. Honeyville was made up of two log houses, two little sheds, a rickety old barn, and a small chicken coop surrounded by a few acres of cleared land. In one of those houses lived a family of seven people—father, mother, three boys, and two girls. The mother and the two little girls, Nina and Dot, were Christians, and they often sang songs in praise to God. They learned the songs from an old hymn book which they dearly loved.

One morning in late autumn the mother sent Nina and Dot on an errand to her sister's home three and a half miles away. The first two miles took the girls through thick woods, while the rest of the way led past houses and through small clearings. Their mother told the girls to start back in time to get home before dark because many wild animals—bears, mountain lions, and sometimes even panthers—were prowling around in the woods. These animals were hungry this time of year because they were getting ready for

winter when they would "hole up" in some cozy cave or hole for their long winter's nap.

The girls started off to their aunt's house, happily chasing each other along the way. They arrived just as the sun was reaching noon, and they enjoyed visiting with their aunt and playing with her new baby. After dinner, their aunt was so busy and the children were so happy playing that the time passed more quickly than they realized. Before they knew it, the clock was striking four. Then Nina and Dot hurriedly started for home, bringing with them the items their mother had sent them to borrow from their aunt. They knew they must hurry if they were going to reach home before dark. Their aunt watched them until they disappeared around a bend in the path, anxiously wishing there was someone to go with them.

The girls made good time until they came to the long stretch of thick woods high on the mountain path. The sun was still sending its beams of light all around them, although the shadows were growing longer.

"I know where there is a big patch of wintergreen berries right by the road," Nina told her sister. "Let's pick some for Mama. We'll have time." So they climbed over a few stones and logs, and sure enough, there was a large patch of berries. They picked berries and talked and even played hide and seek among the bushes for a little while.

When they once more started down the path toward home, the sun was sinking low in the west, and the trees were throwing even longer shadows over the path. They had walked about halfway home when Dot began to feel tired and afraid. Nina tried to cheer her up.

"One more long hill, and we'll be home," she told her sister.

But now they could see the sun shining only on the very tops of the trees on the hill, and the path in the woods was already in twilight. Often as they played around the house, each would try to scare the other by saying, "Oh, I see a bear up the road!" Or, "I see a wolf!"—and pretending to be afraid.

So now, Dot said, "Let's scare each other. You try to scare me."

"All right," replied Nina. Then pointing up

the path, she said, "Oh, look up the path by that black stump. I see a . . ."

She didn't finish what she had been going to say, because suddenly, from almost the very spot she had pointed out, a large panther stepped out of the bushes. He turned his head first one way and then the other. Then, as if seeing the girls for the first time, he crouched down in the path. Like a cat after a bird, he began crawling, sneaking along the ground toward Nina and Dot! The girls stopped with their hearts in their throats, and Dot began to cry.

"On, Nina," she breathed in a half-smothered whisper, "let's run!"

But Nina thought about the long, dark, lonely road behind them. And she thought about how fast a panther can run. And she knew that running was useless. Then she remembered what her father had said about showing fear to animals.

"No," she told Dot. "Let's try to get past it and not let it know that we are afraid." She took her little sister's hand. "God will help us."

Slowly, the two little girls began moving toward the panther. When the children moved, the big cat stopped and straightened up. Then crouching once again, he moved slowly, uneasily toward them. When they had almost reached him, Nina who was closer to him than was Dot, could see his body tensing to spring upon them. All at once she remembered hearing that a wild animal would not attack someone who was singing. What should she sing? She tried to think of a song—any song. But her mind was blank. In despair she breathed a short prayer to God for His help. As she did so, she looked up and caught a glimpse of the last rays of the setting sun shining on the tops of the trees on the hill, and she began to sing:

"There is sunlight on the hilltop,
 There is sunlight on the sea, . . ."

Dot joined in the song. At first, their voices were faint and trembling, but by the time the girls had taken a couple of steps and had drawn opposite the panther, the words of the song rang out sweet and clear.

The panther sank down. Then he straightened up to his full height, his eyes never leaving the girls. His tail had been lashing and switching back and forth, but now it grew still, and he seemed to be listening to their voices as they sang. Hand in hand, the sisters inched their way past the great cat.

"O the sunlight! beautiful sunlight!
 O the sunlight in the heart!"

How sweet the words sounded as they echoed and reechoed through the woods. As the children neared the top of the hill, the rumbling sound of a wagon fell on their ears, and they knew that help was near. But they kept on singing. Soon the wagon came into view; the girls looked back down the path over which they had just come. The panther was disappearing into the woods!

Their mother had been worried when the girls didn't arrive home before it began growing dark. All afternoon, she had gone to the road from time to time, anxiously looking for Nina and Dot, and each time she had been disappointed. Finally, she couldn't wait any longer and took the wagon to meet them. As she neared the summit of the hill, she heard them singing:

"O the sunlight! beautiful sunlight!
 O the sunlight in the heart!
Jesus' smile can banish sadness;
 It is sunlight in the heart."

At first, a happy smile of relief passed over Mother's face, but it faded as she listened. There was such an unearthly sweetness in the song, a note so strong and clear that it seemed like the music of angels rather than her two little girls. The song stopped, and the children appeared over the brow of the hill. She saw their white faces and hurried toward them. When they saw her, how their little feet flew! Trembling and out of breath, they could hardly speak.

But what a joyful season of worship they had that night! And what meaning that dear old song has had for them ever since!

A few days later, some hunters killed the panther that had given Nina and Dot such a fright. But they never forgot what happened that evening on the mountain path when God sent His angels to save them from a panther.

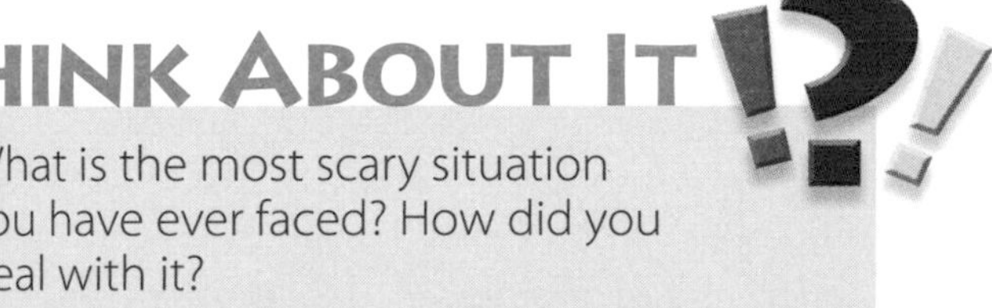

Think About It

- What is the most scary situation you have ever faced? How did you deal with it?
- Can you think of a time when God protected you from danger?

Paying Too Much for a Whistle

THRIFT · GOOD JUDGMENT

Have you ever heard someone say, "He paid too much for his whistle"? Have you wondered what they meant? "Paying too much for your whistle" is a way of saying that you've spent money foolishly for something you thought you wanted but that really wasn't worth what you paid.

Do you know where this saying came from?

You've heard of Benjamin Franklin. You've heard how he flew a kite in a rainstorm to learn more about lightning and electricity. (By the way, this is definitely NOT a good idea! Franklin was lucky he wasn't killed by lightning.) Maybe you've heard how he invented a lot of things and how he was one of the men who helped the United States of America win its freedom from Great Britain. Maybe you've heard how he wrote a lot of wise sayings. One of these sayings was, "A penny saved is a penny earned." He also wrote, "Early to bed and early to rise makes a man healthy, wealthy, and wise." So, Benjamin Franklin was known for being careful, hardworking, and thrifty.

But he also was responsible for the saying, "You paid too much for your whistle." Here's how it happened.

When Ben was seven years old, his mother gave him some pennies. It was the first spending money little Ben Franklin had ever had. He felt very rich and very happy. His mother told him he could go to the store and buy anything he wanted—as long as it didn't cost more money that he had.

So, Ben hurried off to the store to see what he might buy with his pennies. On the way, he met another little boy. This boy had a whistle. He was blowing his whistle as loud as he could. It was a beautiful whistle too. It was bright and shiny, and it made a loud, shrill noise. *How much fun it would be,* little Ben Franklin thought, *to have a whistle like that and blow it as loud as I could!* In fact, he couldn't think of anything he wanted more.

So, he ran to the store just as fast as his legs would carry him. "Do you have whistles?" he asked the shopkeeper.

"Indeed, I do," the man replied. "I have all kinds of whistles. I have wooden whistles and tin whistles. How much do you want to pay for a whistle?"

"I'll pay all the money I have," Ben said quickly, laying all his pennies on the counter. "Is that enough?"

"Take any whistle you like," the shopkeeper said. Ben looked at all the whistles. He saw a tin one that was bright and shiny. He blew it, and it made a loud, shrill noise—just like the whistle he had seen the boy blowing in the street. This was exactly the whistle he wanted. So, he took it and left the store.

Ben walked down the street toward home, blowing his new whistle just as loud as he could. This was fun! He was having a great time.

"Listen to my new whistle!" he called to his brothers and sisters when he got home. And he blew a loud blast.

"How much did you pay for it?" they asked.

"I gave the shopkeeper all my pennies," Ben replied. "Isn't it a beautiful whistle?"

But Ben's brothers and sisters laughed at him. "You paid four times more than you should have," they told him. "You could have bought your whistle and still have had several pennies left over."

Ben looked at his little treasure. The words kept ringing in his ears—*"You paid four times more than you should have."* He thought about all the other nice things he could have bought with the extra pennies. But now it was too late. Ben felt so disappointed that he sat down and cried. He didn't even enjoy blowing his new whistle very much. But he had learned a good lesson.

"Never mind, Ben," his father said to cheer him up. "Next time, you'll know better than to pay too much for your whistle."

And that's where the saying started—"You paid too much for your whistle."

We all have to live and learn. Ben Franklin grew up to be a very wise man, but he never forgot about the day he spent all his pennies for a whistle. And when he was tempted to buy something he really didn't need, he would say to himself, "Don't pay too much for your whistle." And he would save his money instead.

Think About It !?!

- Have you bought something and found out later it wasn't worth what you paid for it? How did you feel?
- How can you be sure that the things you want are really worthwhile things to have?

The Missing Glasses

TRUST IN GOD

Fred stared as hard as he could, but the words on the blackboard still seemed far away and blurry. He tried scrunching up his eyes really small and seeing if that would help. And it did. He could make out some of the words, but even with his eyes scrunched up, he couldn't read the whole sentence. All school year, it had been getting harder and harder for Fred to see well. He often missed catching the ball when the kids played at recess because he didn't see it coming in time.

At last, Fred told his mother about his problem. His mother made an appointment right away with the eye doctor to have Fred's eyes examined. The doctor looked in his eyes with a bright light. He took Fred to a dark room and put him in a chair. Then he showed Fred some letters on the wall. There was a large letter "E" at the very top. It was large and black, and Fred could see it clearly. There were more letters that grew smaller and smaller until Fred couldn't see what they were at all; he could just see that there were lines of dark smudges on the wall.

"Cover your right eye," the doctor said, "and read the letters on the third line for me." Fred started reading the letters. He could tell what some of them were, but others he couldn't see very well at all. Then the doctor had Fred cover his left eye and read the lines.

After Fred read the letters as far down the wall as he could, the doctor placed something in front of Fred's face that looked like a super-large pair of glasses with lots of dials and lenses and numbers on them. The doctor moved things around on the machine and then had Fred look through the lenses at the same letters on the wall. "How does that look?" he asked.

"I can see more letters," Fred told him. So, the doctor had Fred read as many letters as he could looking through the machine. Then he changed some more things on the machine and had Fred look at the letters again. "Is that better still?" the doctor asked.

Fred looked carefully at the letters. "Yes," he said. "I can see even more letters now." The doctor repeated this process several times.

At last, the doctor finished examining Fred's eyes. "Well, your son definitely needs glasses," he told Fred's mother. He wrote some numbers on a pad of paper. Then Fred and his mother picked out some frames that fit Fred. "Your new glasses will be ready in a few days," the doctor said. "We'll call you when they are ready."

At first, Fred thought it would be fun to wear glasses. After all, his mother wore glasses, and she didn't seem to mind. And when his new glasses arrived and he put them on, Fred was pleased at how much better he could see. Everything looked clearer. He could see what the teacher wrote on the blackboard now, and he could see the ball coming in time to catch it.

But there were some things about his new glasses that Fred didn't like. "Mother, my nose and ears are sore," Fred complained about three days after he started wearing his glasses. "My glasses are rubbing sore spots on my ears and nose!"

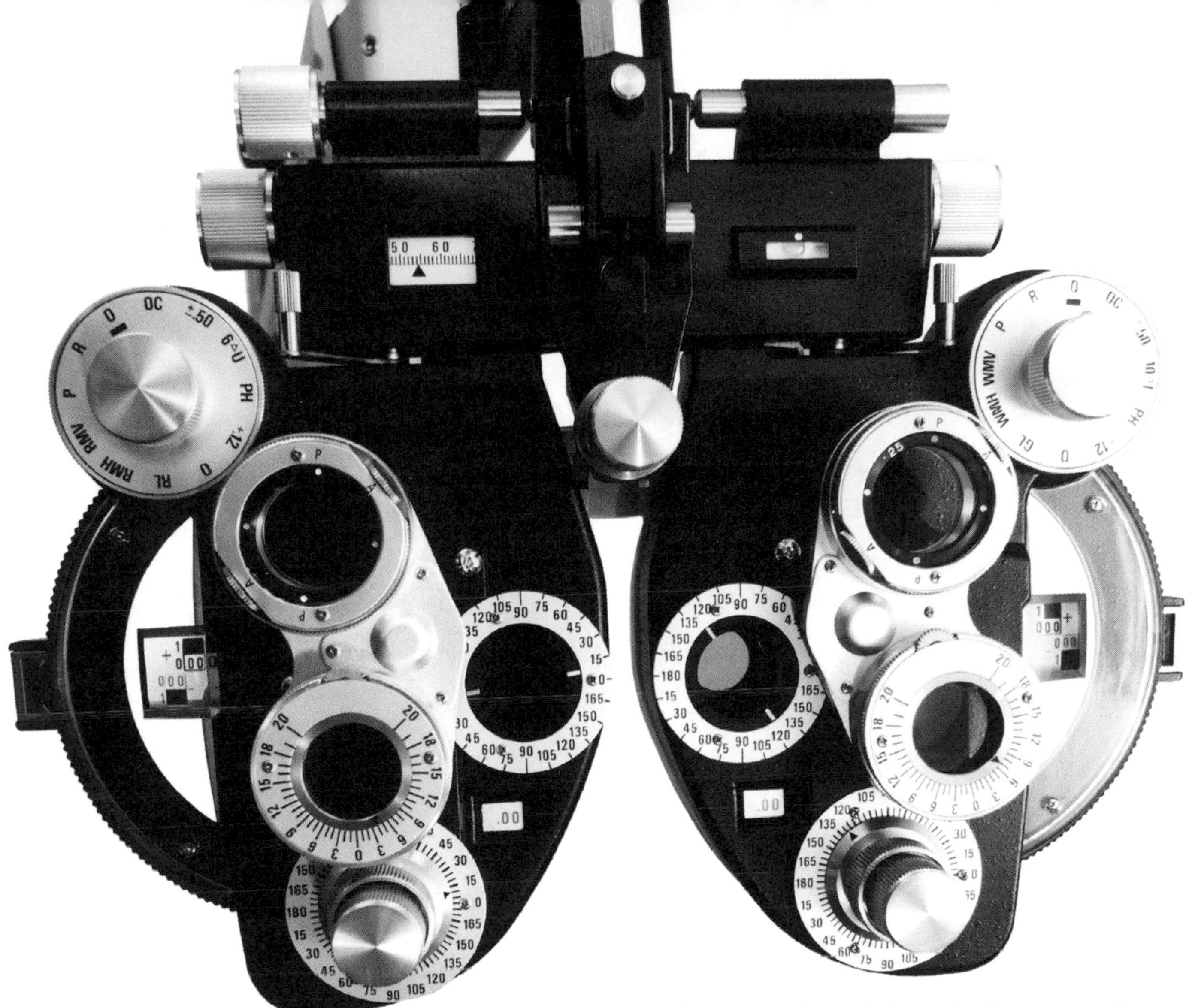

So, Mother put some salve on the sore spots and helped Fred adjust his glasses so that they didn't rub his ears so much.

"Always take good care of your glasses," Mother said. "Keep them clean and put them away in a safe place at night. They cost a lot of money, and you need to be careful with them. I don't have the money to buy new ones if something happens to them."

Fred did try to be careful. One afternoon, about two weeks after he got his new glasses, his mother asked him to help her in the garden. Fred liked to help his mother, and he especially liked to help pick the beans and tomatoes and corn and cucumbers and all the things his mother grew in her large garden. Fred liked to help pick the vegetables because he knew his mother would use them to cook good things for him to eat. So, Fred and his mother went to the garden with big baskets to pick the vegetables that were ripe.

"You take this side," Fred's mother told him, "and I'll start on the other side of the garden."

"OK," Fred agreed. Up and down the rows they went, filling their baskets with good things to eat. After a while, Fred's mother called, "I'm finished over here. I'm going in the house. Bring your basket in when you've finished."

"All right," Fred called back. "I have three more rows to finish."

Before long, Fred came into the kitchen where his mother was washing the things she had picked in the garden. She looked up as Fred put his basket on the counter. "Let's see how much you picked," she said. Then she looked at Fred. "Fred!" she said. "Where are your glasses?"

Fred put his fingers up to his face. "Oh!" he said in surprise. "I forgot! They were hurting my nose, and I took them off for just a minute to rub the sore spot. I must have forgotten to put them back on. But I know where I put them, because I had just stopped to get a rock out of my shoe. And I put my glasses down right there. So I'm sure I can find them again."

"Then run back out to the garden right now," said Mother, "and get them."

Fred quickly went back to the garden and found the spot where he was sure he had left his glasses. *But they weren't there!* Fred looked underneath the plants nearby. No glasses. He looked further around the spot. Still no glasses. He moved a little way down the row and looked again. He became worried and began looking all up and down the row. Before long every spot in the garden began to look like every other place Fred had already looked. And he couldn't find his glasses!

Fred's mother came out to the garden and helped him search. But she couldn't find the missing glasses either.

It was getting dark by now. Mother looked sad, and Fred felt almost like crying even though he was too old to cry. He knew how important it was to find his glasses.

"Let's look some more," he urged.

"But, Fred," Mother replied, "the sun is almost down; there isn't much light left. And besides, we've looked everywhere we can think of already."

"I know something we haven't done," Fred said all at once. "We haven't prayed. Jesus knows where my glasses are, and He knows how much we need to find them. Let's ask Him to help us."

Mother felt a little ashamed that she hadn't thought to pray herself and that Fred had had to remind her. "Of course," she said. "We can pray."

So, Mother and the tired boy knelt down right there in the dirt between the rows of beans. Mother prayed first. Then Fred added, "Jesus, I need my glasses because we don't have enough money to buy new ones. Please help us to find them."

"Now," Fred said, getting to his feet, "let's look again. I know Jesus is going to show us where they are."

He and his mother started down the row of beans—the same row of beans they had already searched once or twice before. They hadn't gone twenty feet until Fred shouted, "There they are! I knew Jesus would help me." And sure enough—there were Fred's glasses, lying just where he had set them down earlier. The lenses were glistening in the last rays of the setting sun.

Now some people may say that Fred found his glasses because the sun happened to shine on them at just the right moment. But Fred doesn't believe that. And neither does his mother. They believe that Jesus helped them find Fred's glasses when they asked Him to.

- Have you ever lost something valuable? Did you find it?
- Does God always help us find something we have lost—or solve some other problem? Why or why not?

LITTLE BILL'S VISIT

RESOURCEFULNESS

This is a true story about an elephant who went to Mr. and Mrs. Brown's house for a visit—and enjoyed himself so much he didn't want to leave! Of course, Mr. and Mrs. Brown wanted him to leave, but Little Bill (that was the elephant's name) didn't realize that they weren't enjoying his visit as much as he was—so he made himself right at home!

It all happened a long time ago in New York City.

Along one side of a quiet street where there were many apartment buildings was a large stable. The stable doors weren't opened very often because the stable belonged to a man who ran a circus, and he

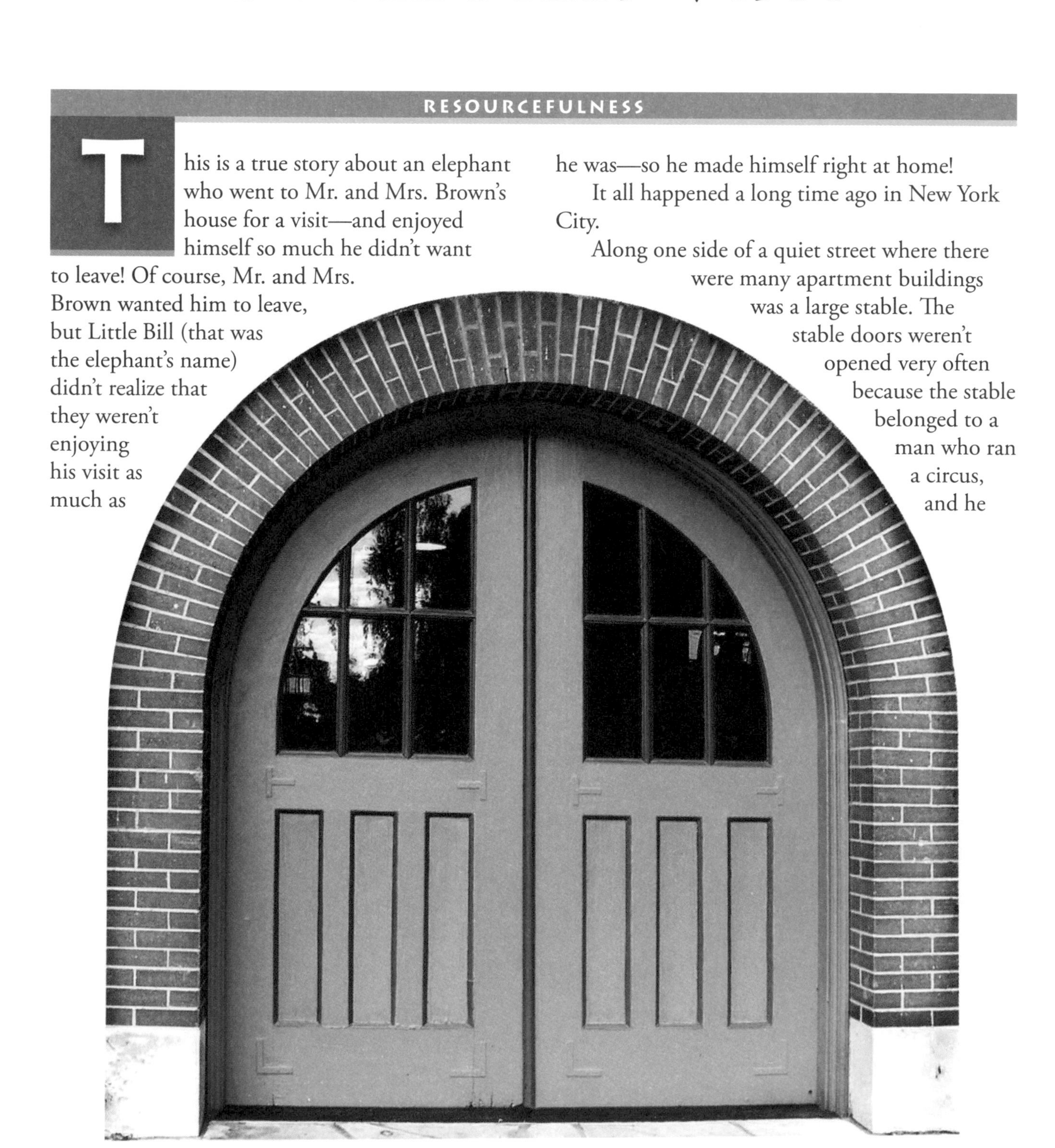

kept his young elephants in the stable until they were old enough to learn tricks and be part of the circus.

Now, above the stable were some apartments where Mr. and Mrs. Brown lived with their family. The owner of the elephants hired Mr. Brown to take care of them in the stable below.

One day, Little Bill, the baby elephant, decided he would like to know more about the big world outside the stable. He could hear sounds coming from the street outside, but he couldn't see outside. And he wanted to know what was going on. Elephants, you see, are very intelligent—and very curious—animals. And Little Bill was just as intelligent and just as curious as any other elephant.

This particular morning Mr. Brown had gone away on an errand, leaving his wife and their children at home. In the stable below, Little Bill decided to go on an errand of his own. He would go for a visit to the apartment above the stable and see what he could see.

He discovered that the only way out of the stable was to open an inside door. He tried and tried to unlatch the door with his trunk. And at last he did. He opened the door and marched through it into a little hallway. At the end of the hall were some narrow stairs leading to the Brown's apartment. No one knows how Little Bill managed to squeeze up the stairs—because even though he was a very small elephant, he was still an elephant, and even a small elephant is a large animal! But Little Bill made his way up the stairs somehow. At the top of the stairs he saw an open door. Little Bill went through the door and into a large room where Mrs. Brown was preparing lunch.

Mrs. Brown thought she heard a noise behind her, so she looked around, and there was Little Bill! Mrs. Brown was so scared she didn't know what to do. She couldn't get past Bill to the door, so she ran to the open window and screamed as loud as she could! All the neighbors ran to their windows and doors and looked out to see what the screaming was about. They saw Mrs. Brown crying out, "Help! Help!" And over her head they could see Little Bill's trunk waving out the open window.

Now, Little Bill wasn't going to hurt anyone. He just wanted to have a good time. He just wanted to breathe the fresh air from the window, so he put his trunk out the window over Mrs. Brown's head and waved it back and forth.

Once in a while, Little Bill would go back into the kitchen and drink some water from the sink. He upset some dishes, but he did step around the room as carefully as he could.

Poor Mrs. Brown was terribly frightened—especially when Little Bill tried to pick up one of the children in his trunk to play with him.

About this time, Mr. Brown returned home. He was just as astonished as his wife had been to see an elephant in his kitchen. At the same time, Little Bill's owner arrived, as well. He and Mr. Brown tried to think of a way to get Little Bill to leave the kitchen. They tried to get him to go through the door and back down the stairs. But Little Bill was enjoying his visit to the Brown's house very much. He didn't want to leave. At last the two men decided that the only way to get the elephant back to the stable without hurting him was to build a long ramp from the window to the street below.

Several carpenters came with large timbers and boards and nails and hammers. They built a long sloping ramp that wasn't very steep.

By the time everything was ready, people from all over the city had heard about Little Bill's visit to the Brown's house. Several thousand people lined up along the street to see what they called the "free circus." Every now and then they could see Little Bill in the window, and everyone wanted to cheer when they saw him. But Little Bill's owner asked them to keep very quiet so that they wouldn't frighten the elephant.

The carpenters took all the glass out of the low window, and then the owner and Mr. Brown urged Little Bill to step through the window and onto the ramp. The owner walked ahead of him, patting him gently on the trunk and talking softly. Everything went just as they had hoped—until they came to a place where the ramp made a

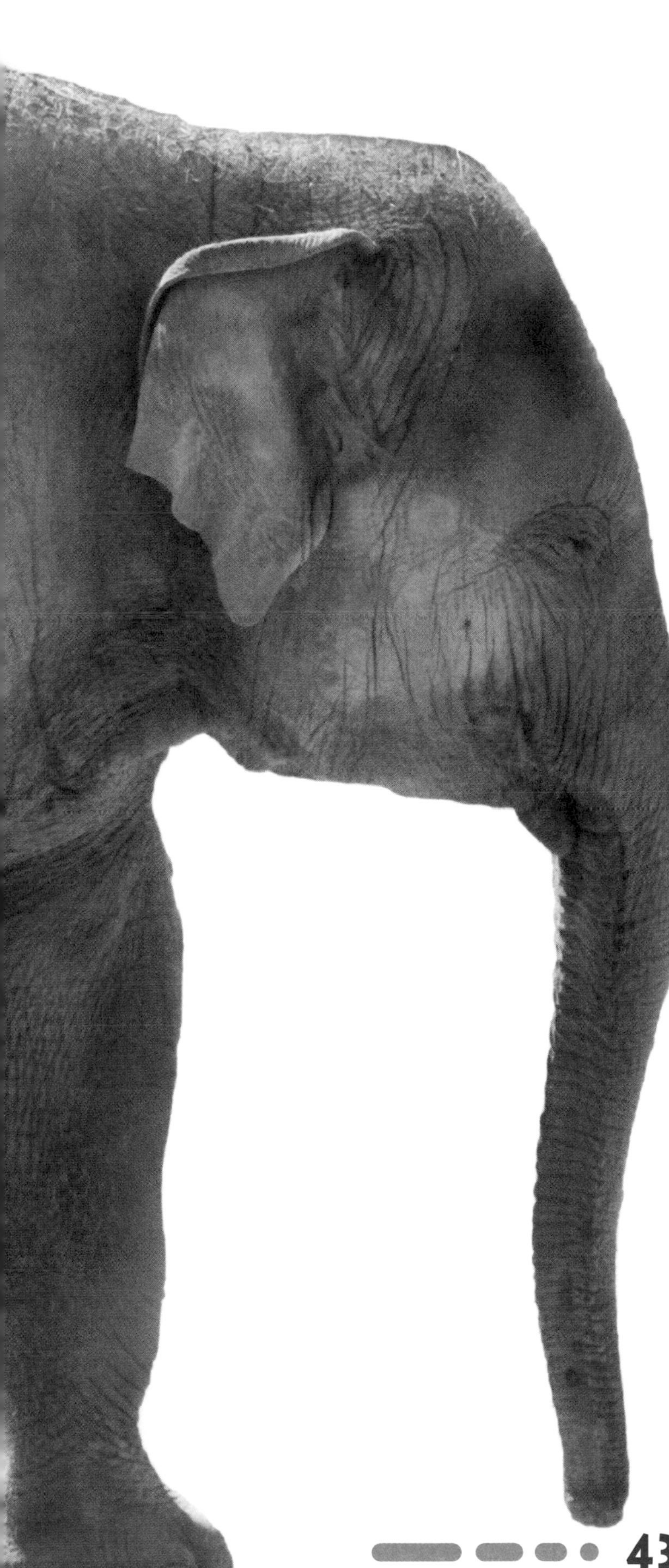

slight turn to cross over a fence and up the street.

Little Bill wasn't sure what to do when he came to the bend in the ramp. He began to turn, but when he stretched out his leg to take the next step, he didn't feel anything beneath his foot! He leaned away from that side of the ramp, pushing his owner over the side! The owner fell to the grass below, but it wasn't very far, and he wasn't hurt.

Little Bill was scared, however. He was afraid he would fall too. Mr. Brown was behind the elephant. He was scared too. He was afraid Little Bill would fall on top of his owner on the grass below. So, he pushed hard against Little Bill in the opposite direction. The poor elephant tried to take another step, but with Mr. Brown pushing against him and the ramp making a slight turn, Little Bill became confused and fell over the side of the ramp, partly on the fence! When he found he couldn't get up, he began trumpeting as loud as he could. He trumpeted so loud that people could hear him from blocks away.

The carpenters came running up and placed some boards underneath Little Bill to make sure he didn't fall any further. Then they brought some bales of hay and stacked them to make a kind of stairs. And Little Bill walked down the stairway of hay until he reached the ground below.

Little Bill was happy to be on the ground again. But no one was happier that he was on the street and out of her kitchen than was Mrs. Brown! She said she would rather take care of a dozen children all day long than one elephant—even one as small as Little Bill!

Think About It

- Would you like to have an elephant in your room? How about a small elephant?
- What is the biggest problem you have ever had to solve?

What Brian Found in His Lunch Box

KINDNESS · THOUGHTFULNESS FOR OTHERS

Ryan, Matthew, Chris, and Tyler sat in the lunchroom at school. They were eager to get out to the soccer field and begin playing, but they were also hungry and ready to eat. The boys began opening their lunches and checking to see what their mothers had packed for them. Matthew unwrapped a thick sandwich and took a big bite. "I wonder why Brian always sits over there in the corner by himself," he said pointing across the room where Brian was eating alone.

"Yeah," agreed Chris. "He never comes around until we're all through eating and ready to go play soccer. I wonder why."

"That's easy," Tyler replied. "He does that because he doesn't want us to see."

"See what?" Matthew asked.

"He doesn't want us to see what he has in his lunch."

"What do you mean? Why would he care if we see?"

"Because," Tyler said, "I don't think he has much in his lunch box at all. I heard my dad say that Brian and his mom are really having it hard since his dad lost his job."

"Yeah, that must be true," Chris said. "Look at his clothes. I wouldn't be caught dead in what he wears." The others laughed.

"I've got an idea," Matthew said. "Tomorrow, let's look in his lunch box and see what he has for lunch. You know he is always the first one in his seat in class, so we can take a look in his lunch box in the closet and still be in our desks before the bell rings."

All the boys agreed to this plan—except for Ryan who hadn't taken part in the conversation at all. "I don't see what fun that would be," he said, wiping his mouth. "It's none of our business what Brian brings for lunch or where he eats it, anyway. I'm not going to go sneaking around looking in his lunch box."

"You're always such a wimp!" Matthew replied. "We're just trying to have a little fun!"

Ryan didn't like being the odd person out, and he didn't like the tone in Matthew's voice. His eyes flashed for just a minute, but then he stood up and said, "Hey, guys! Let's go play some soccer!" And in five minutes the whole playground was alive with kids chasing the soccer ball and playing other games.

The next morning, before the bell rang for class, four faces glanced into the classroom. There, as usual, was Brian, opening his textbook for the first class and arranging his pencils and paper. It took the boys only a moment to hurry to the coat closet where the lunch boxes were kept. Soon the whole group—Ryan included—was gathered around Matthew as he held the mysterious lunch box in his hands.

"It's big enough to hold food for everybody in the school," Matthew declared as he opened it. Inside was a napkin, and underneath the napkin was an apple and a piece of cheese. That was all. Matthew held up the apple with a grin on his face, and the other boys laughed.

"Let's throw it away," suggested Chris, "and

fill his lunch box with rocks or something. It would be fun to watch him open it in the lunchroom."

The boys thought this was a great idea and they quickly took out the apple and the piece of cheese and replaced them with some pebbles and wadded up pieces of paper and other odds and ends. They placed the napkin carefully on top, closed the lunch box, and put it back on the shelf. The boys were in their seats before the bell rang—all except Ryan.

Ryan hung behind as the other boys left the closet. As soon as they were out of sight, he quickly opened Brian's lunch box yet again and took out the trash the boys had placed there. Then he began filling it from his own lunch box. That morning, he had asked his mother to make a second lunch for him to take to school. Of course, she wanted to know why he needed two lunches—and when he told her, she was happy to fix another. Ryan finished putting all the food in Brian's lunch box, placed the paper napkin over it all, and quickly put the box back on the shelf once more. He was only a little late getting to his seat, and no one seemed to notice.

All morning, Matthew, Chris, and Tyler kept looking at each other and trying not to laugh as they imagined Brian's face when he opened his lunch and found the trash they had put there. They looked at Ryan too, but he didn't look back.

At noon, all the kids rushed to pick up their lunches and head for the lunchroom. Matthew, Chris, Tyler, and Ryan sat at their usual table waiting for Brian to show up. They watched him come in, carrying his lunch box over to the corner where he always sat.

"Do you think he suspects anything?" Matthew whispered. "His lunch box is certainly heavier than it was." Ryan could hardly keep from grinning when he heard that.

Four sets of eyes watched Brian sit down.

Four sets of eyes watched him open his lunch box. Four sets of eyes watched as he slowly took the paper napkin out. Then they saw Brian look into the lunch box in surprise. *Our trick is working!* thought Matthew, Chris, and Tyler. Ryan sat back with a smile on his face. His trick was working too.

Brian began pulling food out of his lunch box. There was a sandwich and chips. Fruit. Some nuts and raisins. A large piece of pie. As Brian removed each item from his lunch box, he looked more and more puzzled.

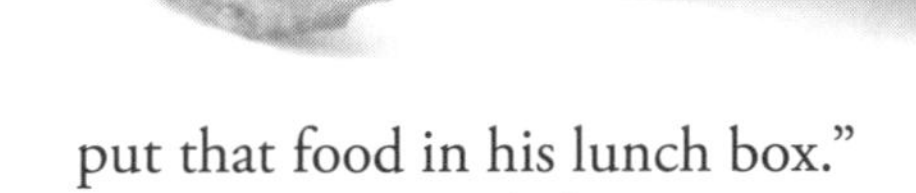

Matthew, Chris, and Tyler were puzzled too. They had been expecting Brian to pull out wadded up paper and other trash. Where had all this good food come from?

Brian was asking himself the same question. *Where has this food come from?* As the other boys watched, Brian put his head down on the table. Tears were starting to run down his face, and he didn't want the others to see. "Maybe he's praying," Tyler said quietly. The other boys slipped out of the lunchroom and went outside to the playground.

"You did it, didn't you?" Matthew asked Ryan. "You put that food in his lunch box."

Ryan just smiled.

"Well, I'm glad you did," Matthew continued. "I was beginning to feel bad about putting all that trash in his lunch box anyway."

"Me too," said Chris.

Tyler nodded. "Yeah," he said. "It's not Brian's fault that his dad lost his job. Besides, I like Brian. It wasn't a very good idea to try to make fun of him."

Just then, Brian came outside. He was smiling now. And he wasn't hungry any more. "Let's go play soccer," he said as he came up to the four boys who were waiting for him.

"Yeah!" they all replied. "Let's play soccer!"

Think About It!?!

- Do you know someone that other kids make fun of because he or she doesn't have nice clothes or is different from everyone else?
- Why do you think the Bible tells us that we should treat people the way we would like to be treated ourselves?

Cornelia's Jewels

CONTENTMENT · UNSELFISHNESS · CHEERFULNESS

Once upon a time in the city of Rome lived a noble woman whose name was Cornelia. She lived more than one hundred years before Jesus was born. Cornelia had two fine sons. The name of the older boy was Tiberius Gracchus. The younger boy's name was Caius Gracchus. Their father, whose name was also Tiberius Gracchus, was one of the leading men in Rome. When the boys were quite young, their father died.

The father's death was a terrible blow to Cornelia. But she was brave, as well as beautiful and cultured. In those days, the noble ladies of Rome wore beautiful dresses and expensive jewels. Cornelia was not as rich as many of the ladies she knew, but she was a sensible woman. She willingly went without jewels and expensive clothes. She would rather spend her money to educate her sons. She made up her mind that her sons should have the best education that Rome could give. She wanted them to become good, useful men.

Cornelia had many friends, and she enjoyed having her friends visit her. Even kings often sat at her table. She was a charming hostess, and her friends were happy to come to her house and be her guests. Cornelia never talked about how sorrows or how hard it was to raise her sons without her husband to help her. Her wonderful cheerfulness and gentle courtesy made her greatly loved by everyone.

One bright morning, a lady friend came to visit Cornelia. She was beautifully dressed. She wore lovely pearls and flashing diamonds. Cornelia was simply dressed in a plain white robe. No rings or necklaces glittered on her fingers or about her neck. Instead of flashing jewels in her hair, her long, soft hair was gathered up in brown braids that crowned her head. She took her friend for a walk among the flowers and trees in her beautiful garden.

Cornelia's sons, Tiberius and Caius, were standing in the vine-covered summer house. They were looking at their mother and her friend.

"Isn't our mother's friend a handsome lady?" said Caius to Tiberius. "She looks like a queen."

"She is not half as beautiful as our mother," replied Tiberius who was nine years older than his little brother. "She has a fine dress, but her face is not so noble and kind as our mother's is. It is our mother who is like a queen."

"You're right," answered the younger boy. "No woman in Rome looks as much like a queen as does our mother."

Soon Cornelia came down the garden path to speak to the boys. She looked into her sons' proud eyes with a loving smile. "Boys," she said,

"I have something to tell you."

They bowed before her as Roman boys were taught to do.

"What is it, Mother?" they asked.

"When you come home from school today, you are to dine with us here in the garden."

Again they bowed as politely as if their mother really were a queen. Then they left the garden and went to school.

While they were gone, Cornelia's friend opened a wonderful little box of jewels that she had brought. She wanted to show them to Cornelia. Carefully, she picked up first one shining jewel and then another. She showed Cornelia their beautiful colors. She told her of their great value. There were diamonds and pearls and rubies and many other kinds of gems. They were indeed beautiful.

At last she looked up at Cornelia and said, "Is it true, Cornelia, that you have no jewels? Is it true, as I have heard, that you are too poor to own them?"

Just then, Tiberius and Caius came in from school.

"No, I am not poor," answered the fond mother as she drew her two boys to her side. "Here are my jewels! They are worth more than all the expensive gems you have shown me."

Tiberius and Caius Gracchus grew to be great men in Rome. They stood for what they knew was right. They tried to pass laws that would help the poor. Tiberius helped the common people find comfortable homes. Caius helped them to be able to buy enough food so they wouldn't go hungry. They both worked hard to make Rome a better place to live. And that is why the world still likes to hear the story of Cornelia's "jewels."

Think About It ?!

- What are some things that are more precious to you than money or jewels?
- Is it more fun to enjoy the things you have—or to always be wanting something you don't have?

A Surprise for Mr. Ciprioni

FRIENDSHIP · KINDNESS · GRATITUDE

Josh and Sarah were going to school. On the way they saw Mr. Ciprioni standing in front of his bakery. He had on his tall white baker's hat. "Good morning, children," he called.

"Good morning!" Josh and Sarah replied. They were glad Mr. Ciprioni had come to live on their street. They had heard their parents talking about how Mr. Ciprioni had come to America from another country and how he had to leave everything behind when he came.

"I wonder what Mr. Ciprioni will have in his window this morning," Sarah said. She and Josh liked to look in the bakery window each morning on their way to school. They liked to look at all the good things to eat. There were cakes and cookies and doughnuts and pies and bread and rolls and muffins. Soon Josh and Sarah stood in front of Mr. Ciprioni's window.

"Look," shouted Josh, "a parade! A parade of animal cookies!"

Sure enough, a long line of animal cookies was marching along one side of the window.

"I see dogs and cats and chickens and lions and elephants," Sarah said.

"I see a cow and a fat pony," said Josh.

Mr. Ciprioni laughed as he watched the happy children standing in front of his bakery window. "Come inside a minute," he said. "Today, I'm giving every boy and girl an animal cookie. You can pick out which one you want."

"Mmm!" sighed Josh. "They look really good."

"Thank you," said Sarah. "You're really nice to us. I wish you had some children of your own. They could help you bake lots of cookies and pies and cakes."

"Yes, they could," agreed Mr. Ciprioni. "But I don't have so much as even a cat!"

"Well, maybe you will find a kitten to live with you someday," Josh told him.

"I'd want one with a good nose," laughed Mr. Ciprioni. "A good nose to smell a mouse anywhere!"

"We have to go," Sarah said. "We don't want to be late to school. Goodbye, Mr. Ciprioni." And away the two children went, running off to school and holding an animal cookie.

"I wish we could do something nice for Mr.

Ciprioni," Josh said as they walked into their classroom. They sat down at their desks.

"Hello, Miss Gray," said Sarah, smiling at her teacher. "We saw a parade this morning!"

"A parade of animal cookies in Mr. Ciprioni's window," added Josh.

"Oh," laughed Miss Gray, "I don't think I've ever seen a cookie parade."

"Mr. Ciprioni is giving every boy and girl who comes by his bakery today an animal cookie," said Josh. "What can we do for him?"

"Let's ask all the other boys and girls in our classroom," suggested Miss Gray. Then she told all the children in the class to pay attention. "Before we begin our lessons," she said, "Josh and Sarah have something to tell us."

Sarah walked to the front of the room. "We saw a cookie parade in Mr. Ciprioni's window this morning," she said. "Mr. Ciprioni has baked lots of cookies for us today. He used to do this in his

own country before he came to America."

"Mr. Ciprioni likes children," Josh added. "But he doesn't have any family—not even a cat."

"That's right," Sarah agreed. "Can't we do something nice for Mr. Ciprioni?"

"I know something all of us could do," Emily said. "We could make a book about all the things we've seen in Mr. Ciprioni's window."

"Yeah! That would be fun," the other children shouted.

So, everyone started to work, and by "Show and Tell" time on Friday each child had something ready to put in Mr. Ciprioni's scrapbook.

David had made the covers to go on the outside of the book. The title on the front cover read: TO OUR FRIEND, MR. CIPRIONI.

Maria had drawn a picture and colored it carefully with her crayons. It showed a little store on a busy street.

Elizabeth had written a poem. Here's what she wrote:

"In Mr. Ciprioni's store,
We look for cookies, cakes, and more.
His window shows what he has made
This time—an animal parade!"

Each boy and girl had a picture or a poem or a letter to put in the book. Some had drawn pictures of their favorite cake or animal cookie. Miss Gray tied all the pages together with a big ribbon and fastened it with a red, white, and blue bow.

"It's been a lot of fun making our book," Sarah said. "Now, let's pick out five of us to give it to Mr. Ciprioni." The children chose Sarah and Josh and Maria and Elizabeth and David to give the book to Mr. Ciprioni. On their way to the bakery, they went by Elizabeth's house to get one more gift for Mr. Ciprioni. They put this special gift under Elizabeth's jacket so Mr. Ciprioni wouldn't see it.

When they came to the bakery, Mr. Ciprioni was busy working in front of his store. A few animal cookies still marched along the window.

"We have something for you, Mr. Ciprioni," called out the boys and girls all together.

"For me?" Mr. Ciprioni asked in surprise, as they handed him the book. He looked at it carefully and turned the pages. "I've never seen such a beautiful book," he told them. "Not even in my own country. Thank you very much!" He looked at each picture. He laughed at the pies and cakes and animal cookies the children had drawn.

Just then Elizabeth reached under her jacket. "We have something else for you," she told Mr. Ciprioni. "Josh told us that you don't have one," and she held out something in both hands.

What was it? At first, all Mr. Ciprioni could see was that it was yellow and furry and was moving around. He was surprised. "What is it?" he asked.

"It's a kitten!" the children all shouted at once.

"You said you didn't have even a cat," said

Josh. "And Elizabeth's cat has six kittens, so we want you to have this one. You can name it anything you like."

Mr. Ciprioni took the kitten and held it close to his shirt. The kitten closed its eyes and purred happily. Mr. Ciprioni smiled. "Thank you," he told the children. "This is the nicest gift I've ever had. I'm going to think of a really good name. Do you think this kitten has a good nose to smell mice?"

That night the children were happy because they had done something nice for Mr. Ciprioni. Mr. Ciprioni was happy because now he had a yellow kitten with a good nose. And the yellow kitten was happy because now he had a new home!

THINK ABOUT IT ⁉

- Has someone done something nice for you recently? How did it make you feel?
- What animal would you choose for a pet if you could have any animal you wanted?

A Poor Woman's Prayer

GENEROSITY · TRUST IN GOD

A Christian lady who often helped the poor was sitting alone in her room one winter morning. Soon her daughter came into the room.

"My dear," the mother said to her daughter, "I've been thinking about old Mr. and Mrs. Woods off and on all night. I know they are going through a hard time right now and they could use some help. I wish you would go to the store and buy some groceries to take to them."

"Of course, Mother," the daughter agreed. And she turned to leave.

"Oh, and maybe you should take this too," her mother said, handing her a warm flannel skirt. "It's cold, and Mrs. Woods might need it."

The girl bought several bags of groceries and carried them to the house where Mr. and Mrs. Woods lived. She was just about to knock on the door, when she heard Mr. Woods's voice inside. She could hear him asking God's blessing on the food they were about to eat. She paused and waited until he had finished praying before she knocked.

As she entered the little home, sure enough, there was Mr. and Mrs. Woods at dinner. Mrs. Woods sat on one side of the table, and Mr. Woods sat on the other. On the

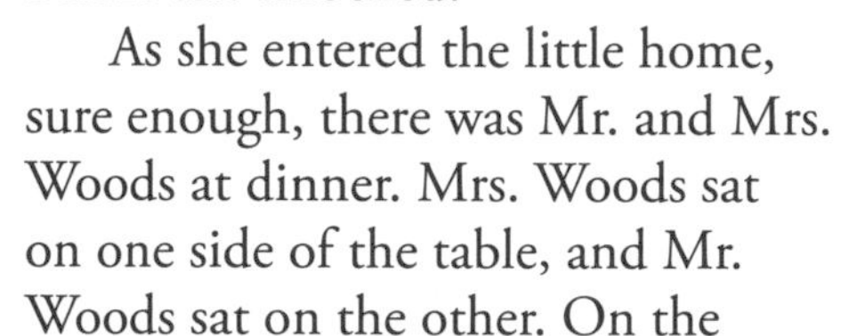

table between them sat their dinner—*one large apple!* This was all the food the old couple had!

With tears in her eyes, the girl set the bags of groceries on the table. And as Mrs. Woods began to fix a nice meal, the young girl listened to their story and their grateful thanks. They told her how they had been sick and how Mr. Woods hadn't been able to work for several weeks and how they were having a very difficult time making ends meet. They told her how they had been pouring out all their troubles to God in prayer and how they had been trusting Him to send them help.

When dinner was ready and their visitor was about to leave, Mrs. Woods went with her to the door. "My dear," she asked hesitantly, "did you bring the flannel skirt?"

In the excitement of getting the dinner ready, the girl had completely forgotten the skirt her mother had sent.

"Why, yes," she said surprised. "I did bring you a flannel skirt. But why would you think that I had?"

"Because, dear," said Mrs. Woods, "when I told the Lord yesterday that we had only one apple left, I also told Him that I needed a warm flannel skirt. And I was just wondering whether He had sent it with you or if He was planning to use someone else to bring it."

Jesus said, " 'Do not worry, saying, "What shall we eat?" or "What shall we drink?" or "What shall we wear?". . . Your heavenly Father knows that you need them. But seek first his kingdom and his righteousness, and all these things will be given to you' " (Matthew 6:31–33, NIV).

Think About It !?!

- What could you do to help someone in your neighborhood? (Helping doesn't always have to mean giving food or clothes!)
- Does God know what ***you*** need?

HONEST GEORGE

HONESTY · DILIGENCE

One day some years ago when people traveled mostly by trains, an energetic shoeshine boy stepped up to a man standing on a platform in Grand Central Station in New York City. "How about a shoeshine, Mister?" the boy asked.

"Well," the man replied, "I could use a shoeshine. But do I have time? I need to catch the Hudson River train."

"There's no time to lose," the boy admitted. "But I can do a good job for you before the train pulls out."

"Are you sure?"

"I'm sure."

"OK," the man agreed. And in two seconds, the boy was down on his knees putting on the polish.

"You won't let the train leave without me, will you?" the man asked anxiously, looking at his watch and then at the train nearby.

"No, I won't, sir," the boy assured him, and he quickly reached for his brushes and began buffing the man's shoes to a high gloss.

"What's your name?" asked the man.

"George Holmes."

"Is your father living?"

"No, sir. He's dead. There's no one except Mother and me. There you are, sir, and the train is starting to move!" George stood up, his job completed.

The man reached quickly into his pocket and took out a dollar. He handed it to George who started to count out his change. But the man was afraid there wasn't time to wait, and he turned and jumped aboard the moving train. George ran alongside with the man's change, but before he could reach him the train picked up speed and pulled away.

George felt bad that he hadn't been able to give the man his change.

Two years later, as George was walking along the street near Grand Central Station, he saw this man again. He was sure it must be him, because George rarely forgot a face. Approaching the man, George asked, "Sir, have you ever been here in New York City before?"

"Yes."

"When?"

"About two years ago."

"Didn't I shine your shoes on the platform here at Grand Central Station?"

"I don't know. There was a boy who shined my shoes. It could have been you."

"And did the train pull out before that boy could give you your change?" George asked.

"Yes, it did," the man replied with a surprised look.

"Well, sir, I'm the boy, and I owe you seventy-five cents. Here is your money. I was afraid I wouldn't ever see you again."

Now, since this is a true story, perhaps you would like to know what became of George. The man whose shoes he had polished was so pleased to find such an honest boy that he asked George where he lived. He took the time to learn about George's situation—how he lived alone with his mother and how they worked hard to make ends meet. The man helped them find a more comfortable place to live—and gave them the money to pay the rent. He set up a fund to make sure George would be able to get a good education. All because of an act of honesty.

Of course, what happened to George doesn't always happen just because we are honest. But even if no one notices, it still pays to be honest. And there are other ways of being honest besides in matters of money. You can be honest with your parents. You can be honest in school. You can be honest with your friends.

Be honest in everything, so that at last God may say to you, "I have been able to trust you in the little things of this life. Now I will make you ruler over great things."

Think About It ?!

- What are some ways to be honest that don't involve money?
- Do your friends and family consider you to be an honest person? Why or why not?

What Happened to Tyler's Knife?

JUDGING · HONESTY · TRUTHFULNESS

Tyler had a new knife. It had a beautiful pearl handle and three sharp, shiny blades that folded out easily. It was just the kind of knife Tyler had wanted for a long, long time—so long he couldn't remember when he had first seen a knife like it and hoped to someday have one of his very own.

Now his dream had come true. Uncle Dan had given Tyler this wonderful knife for his birthday. Already he was finding all kinds of uses for it. There was a piece of string that he needed to cut, a piece of cardboard that he needed to poke a hole in, a rose to cut for his mother, and a piece of wood to whittle. Tyler was sure he would find many things to do with his new knife as the days went by.

He had found the package by his plate at breakfast on the morning of his birthday. As soon as breakfast was over, he began to try out the blades. Tyler was using his new knife to make a peg to fix a toy for his little brother when his best friend, Kevin, came over to play and to wish him "Happy Birthday."

"See my new knife," Tyler exclaimed as soon as Kevin walked into the room.

Kevin took the knife. He turned it over and over, looking at it from every angle. "It's a great knife," he said, laying it down on the arm of the big stuffed chair in the living room. "I wish I had a knife like that."

Together Tyler and Kevin tried to fit the peg into place. "It's still a little too big," Tyler said. "I need to make it smaller." He reached for his knife.

It wasn't on the arm of the chair where it had been just a moment before! Tyler turned to Kevin. "Where's my knife?" he wanted to know.

Kevin looked puzzled. "It was right here. I put it on the arm of the chair. I'm sure I did."

"If you did, it would still be there," Tyler said. "I didn't touch it, and no one else has been here in the room."

"But I did put it there," Kevin insisted, pointing to the place where he had laid the knife. "I laid it right there."

"Then where is it?" Tyler demanded.

"I don't know," said Kevin. "All I know is that I didn't touch it after I put it on the chair."

"But you must have," Tyler argued. "No one else was here, and the knife is gone."

"I didn't take your old knife!" Kevin said, beginning to look worried. "You'd better not say that I did!"

Tyler was getting angry too. "It's not funny

to joke around like that. Give me my knife right now."

"I told you I don't have it," Kevin said.

Tyler ran into the next room. "Mother," he called, "Kevin took my knife, and now he won't give it back. He's going to keep it."

Mother smiled at the angry boy. "There must be some mistake. Kevin wouldn't take your knife. He wouldn't take something that doesn't belong to him."

"But I know he did," Tyler replied. "He stole it. It's gone."

"Wait a minute." Mother sounded serious. "Did you see Kevin take your knife?"

"I gave it to him to look at," Tyler said. "And when I needed it again, he said he had put it on the arm of the chair. But he didn't, because it isn't there. No one else was in the room. So Kevin isn't telling the truth. He took my knife."

"Would you take something that belonged to Kevin?" Mother asked Tyler.

"Of course not!" he exclaimed. "I don't steal."

"Well, Kevin is honest too," Mother said. "I've never known him to take anything that doesn't belong to him. And I'm sure he feels bad that you have accused him of stealing your knife. Let's go see if we can find out what has really happened to it."

When they were in the living room, Mother said, "Kevin, show me where you put the knife."

"Right here," Kevin replied, pointing to the arm of the big chair. "I didn't take it. I really didn't."

"I know you didn't," said Tyler's mother. She turned the chair around and pulled out the seat cushion.

"It isn't there," Tyler said. "I already looked."

Mother kept right on looking. She turned the chair on its side. When she did so, the boys heard a thump down inside the chair. Mother reached in among the springs. When she pulled out her hand—there was Tyler's knife!

Tyler looked stunned. "So, Kevin didn't have it," he said. "But how did it get down in the middle of the chair?"

He thought a minute. "I know," he said. "I sat on the arm of the chair for a minute. I must have knocked the knife off so that it fell down the side of the cushion." He turned to Kevin. "I'm sorry I said that you stole it."

"That's all right," Kevin answered. "I felt bad because you thought I'd taken it. But it's all right now."

"But it might not have been all right," Tyler said. "What if we hadn't found it for a long time?

I'd have gone on thinking you were a thief. I guess I should be more careful before I jump to the wrong conclusion."

"That's a good idea," his mother agreed. "You almost lost a good friend because you made up your mind before you really knew the facts."

Think About It ?!

- Are things always what they seem to be?
- What can you do to keep from jumping to the wrong conclusion?

GREYFRIAR'S BOBBY

LOYALTY · FAITHFULNESS

In the city of Edinburgh, Scotland, everybody knows about Bobby. Visitors like to see his statue standing in the city. The monument to Bobby is a fountain, and on the top of the fountain stands a bronze statue of Bobby. Now, this Bobby is not a boy, but a dog—a Scotch terrier whose story is very interesting.

Years and years ago Bobby and his master came regularly into the marketplace near Greyfriar's church in Edinburgh. In fact, every day when the big gun at the castle boomed out at noon, Bobby and his master crossed the marketplace to Traill's restaurant for lunch. Bobby was always given a bone and a piece of bread for his lunch. This continued for some years. Then one day Bobby's master died and was buried in Greyfriar's churchyard nearby.

Three days after the funeral, when the big gun went off at noon, Bobby showed up as usual at the restaurant, a picture of hunger and grief. The kind owner recognized him and gave him his usual bone and piece of bread. The next day, the dog came again, and the restaurant owner became curious and followed him. Where do you think Bobby went?

That's right. He went straight to his master's grave in the churchyard, where he ate his piece of bread and then lay down with his bone to keep watch over his master.

Some people took Bobby home with them and cared for him, but he wouldn't stay at home. Three times he made his escape, and each time he came back to the churchyard to continue his watch over his master's grave. Now, there was a sign on the churchyard gate: "No dogs allowed." But the old man who looked after the grounds was too kindhearted to make Bobby go away. So, there he stayed, day and night, taking refuge in the shelter of one of the big grave stones when there was a storm. No one could coax him away, so a little house was built for him, and every day at noon Bobby trotted from the churchyard to the nearby restaurant for his dinner—a bone and a piece of bread.

After some time, a new law was passed requiring all dogs in the city to be licensed and to wear a collar. Bobby had no license, of course, so he was picked up and taken to the animal shelter. What do you think happened next?

Bobby had become so well known by this time that the mayor of Edinburgh himself paid the license fee for the little dog, and he kept on paying it every year. He also bought Bobby a shiny new collar, which you can see today in a museum in the city.

So, Bobby took up his watch again beside his master's grave, and there he stayed until his death. When Bobby died, he was buried beside his master. His friends put up a small headstone in his memory. And on the little fountain at the street corner near the churchyard, where the bronze figure of Bobby still keeps watch, you can read these words:

A tribute to the affectionate fidelity of Greyfriar's Bobby. In 1858 this faithful dog followed the remains of his master to Greyfriar's churchyard and lingered near the spot until his death in 1872.

From this inscription, can you figure up how many years Bobby watched beside his master's grave? That's right! From 1858 to 1872 is fourteen years. For fourteen years—day and night—the faithful little dog remembered his master and stayed close beside his grave!

That's what a little Scotch terrier did for the sake of love! Isn't God good to give us such faithful and loving pets? And just as this little dog loved his master and obeyed and honored him, you can love and honor your mother and father and brothers and sisters. You can be faithful to them and show them every day how much you love them.

THINK ABOUT IT?!

- What can you do today to show your family that you love them?
- Do your friends know they can count on you?

GRACE DARLING

COURAGE · DETERMINATION · UNSELFISHNESS

Grace Darling was the daughter of a lighthouse keeper. The lighthouse where Grace lived and where her father took care of the light was located on one of the Farne Islands off the northeast coast of England.

Grace couldn't remember a time when she hadn't been near the ocean, and she was no more afraid of the water than you are of the land.

When she had been just a little girl, her father had often taken her in his boat with him as he rowed across the waves from their island to the mainland. As she grew older, he taught her how to row and let her handle the boat all by herself. She became a very good sailor.

One night in 1838 a terrible storm rolled in from the ocean. The fog became so thick that even the bright beams from the lighthouse were swallowed up, and the steamship *Forfarshire* was blown against some nearby rocks and broken in pieces. Many of the people on board the ship drowned, but at daybreak there were nine of the ship's crew still alive and clinging to the wreckage of the ship upon the rocks.

All night long, during the storm, Grace had been worried and unable to sleep. As soon as it was light, she took her telescope and turned it toward the rocks. The storm was fading, but strong winds were still blowing the water into a seething mass of foam. She could see the poor people out on the rocks, trying to stay alive and avoid being pulled into the waves that were still crashing violently against the wreckage.

"Father," Grace cried, "look! A ship is broken up on the rocks, and some of the crew are still alive!"

Her father looked through the telescope at the terrible sight. "Poor souls," he said, "they won't last long."

"But we can't just leave them there," Grace insisted. "We have to take the boat and try to reach them."

"Grace," her father explained. "It's too dangerous. Our little boat wouldn't last two minutes in those waves."

"But we have to try," Grace pleaded. "We can't do nothing. I'll go with you, Father. I can handle one of the oars and you the other. We can do it. I know we can."

At last Grace's father agreed to try to reach the survivors and rescue them. He and Grace put on their storm gear and prepared the boat. Together they launched it into the waves and struggled to keep it afloat in the rough waters and strong winds. Grace's mother anxiously watched them go and prayed that God who "hath measured the waters in the hollow of his hand" (Isaiah 40:12, KJV) would keep her husband and daughter safe and help them bring the poor survivors safely back with them. She remembered how Jesus had once calmed a raging storm with just a word of command, and she offered another prayer that He would care for her loved ones.

As the brave mother watched, the little boat often sank out of sight, but each time it rose again and came nearer and nearer to the wreck. Finally, Grace and her father reached the rocks where the nine survivors were clinging for their lives, nearly dead with cold and fear. One by one, five of the nine managed to climb into the little boat as it tossed up and down on the wild waters. That's all the boat could hold. Then, with Grace and her father pulling at the oars, they made their way back to the lighthouse. Once there, Grace's father and two of the crewmen from the wrecked ship returned to the rocks and carried off the remaining survivors.

The story of this daring rescue and the brave girl who had saved the lives of nine people spread all over the world. Grace was astonished when

letters began arriving at the lighthouse to praise her for what she had done. And not only letters. Packages came as well with presents inside for the girl who had risked her life to save others. She was showered with awards and medals and large sums of money as her story was told and retold in newspapers everywhere. But she refused to take any of the money.

You see, Grace hadn't gone out in the awful storm so that she would be known and admired all over the world. She had gone out to save nine lives who would have died if she had done nothing. That was all she had been thinking of. And it was this unselfish motive that made what Grace did so noble.

This heroic rescue happened many years ago. And Grace herself died many years ago. But her unselfish act still lives. The influence of what she did still touches lives. We can't all show our courage the same way that Grace did. But we all can try to help others whenever we have the opportunity. It takes courage to tell the truth. It takes courage to do something we know we ought to do even if we don't want to do it. It takes courage to keep on when we feel like quitting and complaining. No matter who we are, we all can show courage every day—in big ways and in little ways.

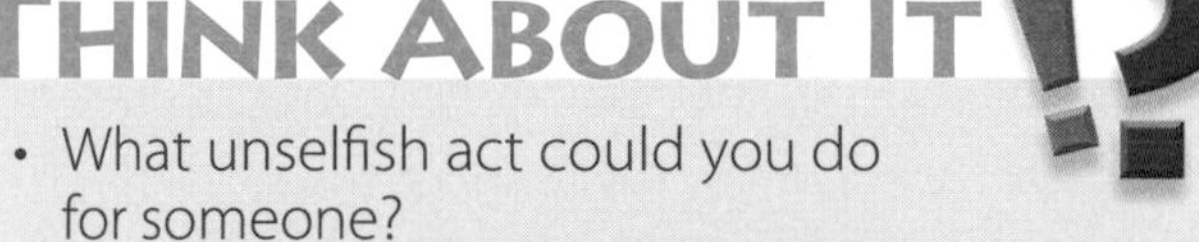

Think About It

- What unselfish act could you do for someone?
- How does a person get courage? How can a person overcome fear?

Androcles and the Lion

KINDNESS TO ANIMALS · GRATITUDE · FRIENDSHIP

Many years ago all the Western world was ruled by one country. That country was Rome. To the people who lived there, Rome was the whole world, and the man who ruled Rome ruled the world. He was called the "emperor." Everyone had to obey the emperor. If they did not obey, they were punished harshly. Often they were made slaves, and many times they were killed.

Androcles was a poor Roman slave. His master was a very cruel man. For a long time Androcles tried to be patient, even though he was a slave. He tried to be happy and do his work well. But no matter how hard he tried, he couldn't really be happy as long as he was a slave. Often he wished he could run away. Maybe he could find another master who would be kinder to him.

But how could he run away without being caught? And where could he go? If he tried to run away and his master found him, he would surely kill him. So, Androcles stayed and tried to be patient.

But finally, Androcles could bear it no longer. He made up his mind that he would rather die than be the slave of so cruel a master. So, one dark night he slipped quietly out of the house. No one heard him. No one saw him. Carefully he crept down the street and out of the town. Then he ran as fast as he could. He didn't know where he was running. He just knew he wanted to get as far away from his master as he could.

When the sun came up, Androcles was many miles from his master's house where he had been so unhappy. He was in the country; he couldn't see any houses or anyone else anywhere. For days he had nothing to eat. He became so weak that he thought he was going to starve. But at least he was no longer a slave.

Finally, Androcles found a cave and went inside. He lay down, and soon he was fast asleep.

Suddenly, a loud noise woke him up. It sounded like a roar, and it sounded very close! Androcles jumped to his feet. At the entrance to the cave he saw a huge lion! What could he do? He was terrified. But he couldn't get away because the lion was standing right in the entrance to the cave. Androcles expected the lion to pounce on him and tear him to pieces. He looked at the lion, and the lion looked at him.

Then Androcles saw that something was wrong with one of the lion's paws. It was swollen and the lion kept licking it. It seemed to be bleeding.

The lion didn't attack him, so Androcles began to be less afraid. Slowly, he moved toward the great beast. The lion looked at him but didn't roar again or bare his teeth. Instead, the lion held up its paw. It seemed to be saying, "Will you help me?"

As Androcles came nearer, he saw that there was a long sharp thorn fastened deep in the lion's paw. He slowly approached, and at last he took the lion's paw in his hands. Carefully, he took the end of the thorn firmly in his fingers. Then with one strong, quick pull—out came the thorn!

The lion growled, but he didn't try to bite Androcles. He just lay down and went to sleep. Androcles watched the animal carefully. At last the lion awoke. He looked at the man beside him. Androcles didn't move a muscle. Then the lion reached out with his long tongue and began licking Androcles' feet and then his hands. He was trying to say "Thank you" to his new friend. Clearly, his paw felt better. It wasn't as swollen as before.

After that, Androcles was no longer afraid of the lion. When night came, the man and the lion lay down together and slept, side by side. The next day the lion left but soon returned bringing food. For three years, Androcles and the lion lived together. Day by day they hunted together for food. Night after night they slept together in the cave. They became good friends, and Androcles was very happy. He was no longer a slave. He no longer had a cruel master.

But one day, some soldiers came and discovered Androcles' cave. They were looking for runaway slaves. They put Androcles in chains and took him back to Rome. There they put Androcles in prison. It was a crime in Rome for a slave to run away from his master. And the punishment was death.

At that time, criminals who were sentenced to death often were made to fight a wild animal such as a hungry lion. Of course, a man was no match for a lion, and the lion always killed the man and devoured him. This was to be the fate of Androcles.

When the day came that Androcles was to face his death in the arena, thousands of people crowded to see the sport. They brought the condemned slave into the arena and gave him a knife to defend himself against the lion. But what use was a knife to meet such a savage beast?

The lions were kept in a cage

below the floor of the arena. They had not been fed in many days, so they were very hungry. Androcles could hear the roaring of the hungry lions even over the noise of the huge crowd. He was afraid and trembling.

Soon the door to the cage was opened and a roaring lion rushed out and bounded into the arena where Androcles was waiting, knife in hand. The great beast ran toward the man—and then he stopped short! He looked at the slave from head to foot. The crowd grew quiet. They didn't know what was happening.

Then they saw an amazing sight. The hungry lion began to gently lick the slave's hands. The

people watched as Androcles put his arms around the lion's neck! They couldn't believe their eyes. The lion rubbed his head against the slave's face. What could it all mean?

The guards asked Androcles to explain what was happening. With his arms still around the lion's neck, Androcles told them that this animal was his old friend. He told them how he and the lion had lived together in a cave.

"No one has ever been a friend to me, except this lion," he said. "We love each other as brothers."

"Let Androcles live," the people all shouted. "Set him free!"

"Let him live; set him free!" echoed from every part of that vast crowd.

"Let the lion go free too!" the cry went up. "Give both man and animal their liberty," the crowd demanded.

The emperor was so delighted with what was taking place that he set Androcles free. He gave him money and made him a present of the faithful lion. For many years, Androcles and the lion lived together in Rome. When people saw them, they would say, "That is the lion who is the friend of the man. And that is the man who is the friend of the lion."

Think About It!?!

- Are kind deeds always repaid with kindness?
- What should you do if you have been nice to someone—and he or she isn't nice in return?

The Secret of William's Success

DILIGENCE · HONESTY · FAITHFULNESS TO GOD

Many years ago, a young sixteen-year-old boy left home to make his way in the world. Everything he owned was tied up in a bundle that he carried in one hand. As he walked along, he met an old neighbor, the captain of a canal boat.

"William," the man called, "where are you going?"

"I don't know," the boy answered. "My folks are too poor to keep me at home any longer, and now I have to make my own living."

"Well," his friend replied sympathetically, "be sure you start right, and you'll get along just fine."

William told the captain that the only business he knew anything about was making soap and candles. (This all happened long ago when people used candles to light their homes at night and often made their own soap!) William had helped his father make soap and candles while he still lived at home.

"Let me pray with you and give you a little advice before you go," said the friendly old man.

They both knelt down right there in the path—William and the old boat captain—and the elderly gentleman prayed earnestly for God to bless William as he started out in life on his own.

After prayer was finished and they stood up, the man told William, "Someone will soon become the leading soap maker in the whole state of New York. It can be you as well as anyone else. Make honest soap. Give a full pound. When you begin making money, give the Lord all that belongs to Him out of every dollar you earn. Be a good man and give your life to Jesus."

When William arrived in New York City, he had difficulty at first finding a job. But at last he was successful. He got a job with a company that made soap. Lonesome and far from home, he remembered what the old boat captain had told him. Then and there, William determined to follow Jesus and be honest in everything. He joined a church in the city. And he remembered what the old man had said about being honest with God. He studied his Bible and found there that God asks His people to give one-tenth of their earnings to Him.

"If the Lord asks for one-tenth," William said to himself, "I will happily give that." And he did. From the very first dollar he earned, William gladly gave ten cents to the Lord.

And he continued to do that. Ten cents of every dollar he made was sacred to God.

Years passed. William worked hard. He was careful and faithful in his work, and it wasn't long before he became one of the company's most valuable foremen. After that, he was promoted to manager. Finally, he was offered a job in the company as a junior partner. After some years, both of the senior partners died, and William became the sole owner of the business.

He made honest soap and gave his customers full measure. All his life, he had followed the old captain's advice and tithed his earning—one-tenth of all he made he gave to the Lord. Now he determined to do the same with his company's earnings. He told his bookkeeper to open an account with the Lord and to transfer one-tenth of everything the company made into this account.

William's company thrived and grew. He became more and more prosperous. His family was blessed. His soap sold well because it was a good product and fairly priced. He grew richer than he had ever dreamed possible. So, William decided to give the Lord two-tenths of all that his company earned—twice as much as the Bible says we should. William prospered even more.

Then he gave the Lord three-tenths, then four-tenths, and five-tenths. It just seemed that he couldn't outgive God's blessings! The more he gave the Lord, the more the Lord blessed him. Before long, William was giving to the Lord far more than he was keeping for himself!

This is the true story of Mr. William Colgate, whose soap and cosmetic products are still found on store shelves everywhere. During his life, William Colgate gave millions of dollars to missions both in the United States and around the world and has left a name that will be remembered as long as time will last.

Think About It!?!

- Do you think God blessed William because he was honest about tithe—or because he worked hard?
- If you earned ten dollars, how much would the Lord's tithe be? What would the tithe be if you earned a hundred dollars?

BRUNO

PERSEVERANCE · DETERMINATION · FAITHFULNESS

Bruno was a large Saint Bernard dog that belonged to a hunter who lived in a cottage in the Alps. The higher parts of these mountains are very rocky and wild, and the paths are steep and dangerous. On the lower slopes are woods and green pastures, and in the valleys far below are beautiful little villages. In summer, the mountains are warm and sunny. But in winter, the roads and paths are deep in snow. Storms and bitter cold can blow in without warning, making travel difficult and life-threatening. This story happened many years ago when the people who lived on these mountains mostly stayed at home in the winter and tried to avoid traveling over the snowy, dangerous mountain paths.

One winter night the hunter came home and found that his youngest child was very sick. There was no medicine in the house, and the nearest doctor lived in the village at the foot of the mountain. But it was clear to the father that his little boy must have help as soon as possible.

Calling his dog, Bruno, the hunter wrapped his heavy coat tightly about him and pulled on his hat and gloves. Then he and his brave dog started down the mountain together. Snow was falling fast, and the hunter's lantern provided just enough light to keep him on the path. Bruno and his master hurried as quickly as they dared down the steep trail. After some time, they reached the village safely and made their way to the doctor's home.

When the medicine was ready, the hunter and his dog went out again into the storm. If anything, the night was even darker than before, and the snow had drifted over the path so that it was more difficult to find their way than it had been earlier when they had come down the mountain. But with the help of his faithful dog, the weary man struggled on until he was almost home. Then his strength began to fail, and he sank down into the snow. Bruno barked and rubbed his master's cheek as if to say "Get up! You have to get up and keep climbing!"

"Yes, Bruno," his master said. "I'll get up and try again." And with all his strength, the hunter struggled to his feet and began wading through the soft, deep snow until he was within a hundred feet or so of his own cottage door. But the snow was falling so hard and the drifts had grown so deep that he couldn't tell where he was. He became confused and thought he had lost his way.

"Bruno," he said, sinking down into the snow again, "I have to stop and rest a minute before I can go on."

Bruno's keen sense of smell told him that they were nearly home. He jumped and barked, and tried every trick he knew to get his master to go on. But nothing he did could rouse the man. He lay in the snow, unable to get up.

Now, it's very dangerous to lie down to sleep in a cold storm and snow. When a person becomes very tired and very cold, sometimes all he wants to do is go to sleep. But it's the cold that is making him feel that way. He may think he will rest for just a few minutes and then get up and keep walking, but usually he goes to sleep and never wakes up! Bruno's master was in danger of that very thing. So, Bruno barked and pulled at his master's sleeve, trying to wake him up and get him to keep moving.

But nothing the faithful dog did seemed to rouse the hunter. He was too tired and too cold. At last Bruno ran toward the nearby cottage and raised his voice in a long howl. The hunter's wife heard him and knew that voice. "My husband needs help," she said to herself and ran from the cottage into the snow. Guided by the dog's cries, she soon found her way to her husband, lying in the snow. Rousing him, she helped support him as he somehow stumbled the last few yards to his door. The precious medicine for his sick child was safely in his pocket.

And so Bruno, the faithful Saint Bernard, saved not only his master's life but the life of his master's little boy.

THINK ABOUT IT

- Have you ever faced a difficult challenge? If so, what kept you going?
- Do you have a friend—animal or human—who would do anything for you?

Jim's Big Decision

HONESTY · DILIGENCE

"Remember," Mrs. Allen told all the boys and girls in the seventh grade, "one week from today we are going to have our final test in American history. The questions will cover everything we've been studying during the last three months, so you'll have to study hard."

All the seventh-graders groaned out loud as they gathered up their books and papers and got ready to go home.

Jim climbed on the school bus and took a seat. He was thinking about the history test and how much studying he was going to have to do if he wanted to get a good grade. He was thinking so hard about the test he hardly noticed when Eric sat down beside him. "What's the matter," Eric asked looking at Jim. "Are you sick or something?"

"No. I'm thinking about that history test next week. We're going to have to spend of lot of time studying."

"Not me," Eric said. "I'm going down to the skateboard park and practice every night this week. I don't have to study for that old test."

"Why not?" Jim wanted to know.

"Because I already know all the questions that will be on it," Eric told him. "Several of the kids in class have them. You just have to be sure you know the answers to those questions, and you'll do fine. You don't have to spend all week studying."

"How do you know the questions?" Jim asked.

Eric looked around carefully and lowered his voice. "George found a copy of the test in the wastebasket last week when he was helping the janitor take out the trash. I guess Mrs. Allen had forgotten to shred it before she threw it away. George managed to slip it out of the wastebasket and put it under his coat without the janitor seeing him. He's selling copies for five dollars. He'll sell you one if you want it. He's keeping it a secret from most of the kids in the class since he doesn't want word to get out. But he would sell you a copy, I'm sure. It's good money for George, and several of us will get a good grade without having to study."

Jim didn't know what to think. He knew what George was doing was wrong. And he knew that to buy a copy of the test would be cheating. But he also knew that he was going to have to spend several hours every night studying to have any chance at all of doing well on the test. And he knew that the test counted a lot toward his final grade in the class. He was tempted to give George five dollars and not have to study.

For a while, a battle was going on in his mind. What should he do? The bus was almost at his stop. Eric was looking at him; he had to make a decision. Should he cheat or should he spend all week studying? The bus was slowing down, and the driver was turning on the flashing red lights. Eric waited for Jim's answer.

"No, Eric," Jim said as the bus stopped. "I don't want a copy of the test. That wouldn't be fair. I want to take the test honestly and do well because I've studied—not because I've cheated."

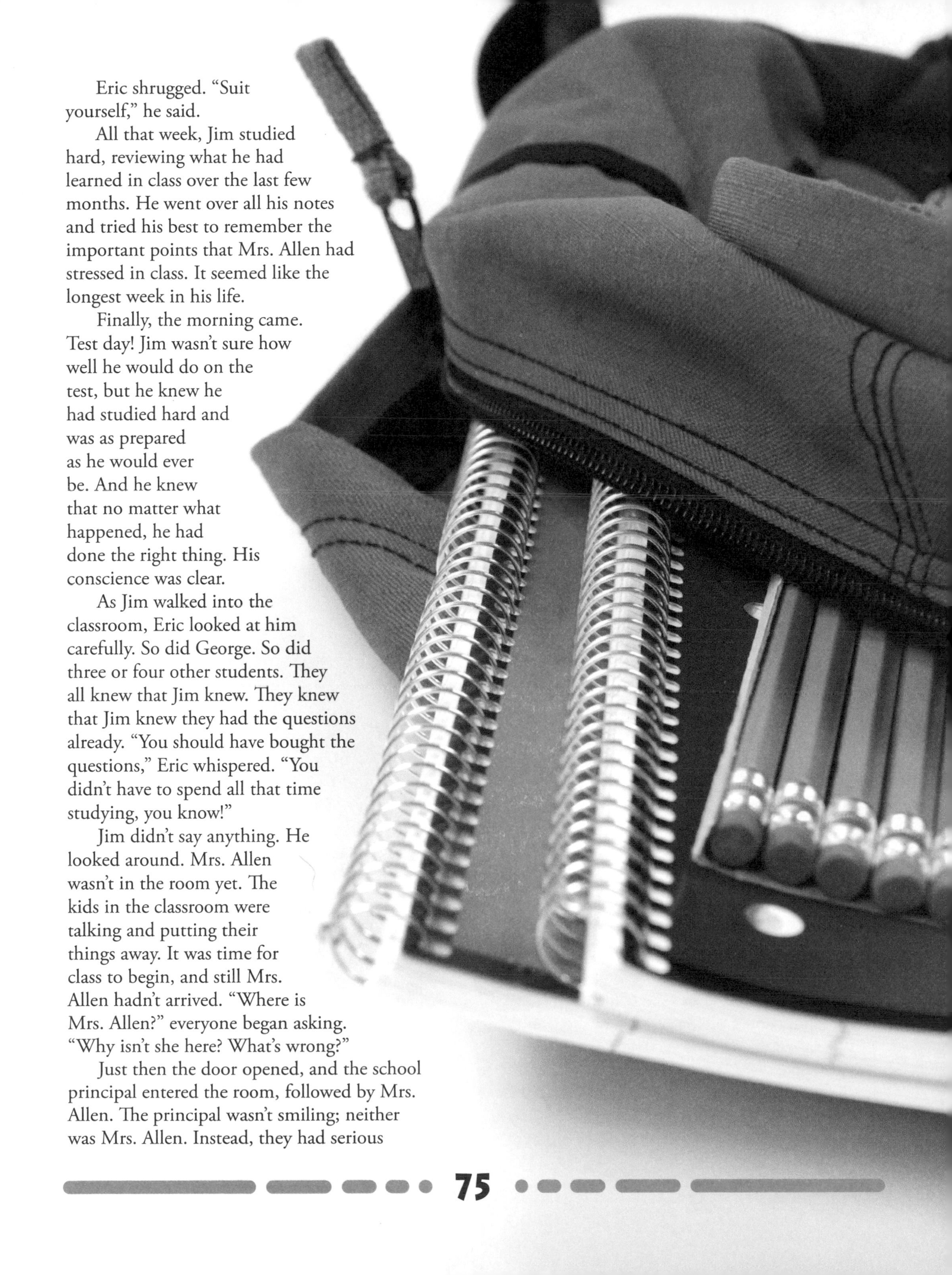

Eric shrugged. "Suit yourself," he said.

All that week, Jim studied hard, reviewing what he had learned in class over the last few months. He went over all his notes and tried his best to remember the important points that Mrs. Allen had stressed in class. It seemed like the longest week in his life.

Finally, the morning came. Test day! Jim wasn't sure how well he would do on the test, but he knew he had studied hard and was as prepared as he would ever be. And he knew that no matter what happened, he had done the right thing. His conscience was clear.

As Jim walked into the classroom, Eric looked at him carefully. So did George. So did three or four other students. They all knew that Jim knew. They knew that Jim knew they had the questions already. "You should have bought the questions," Eric whispered. "You didn't have to spend all that time studying, you know!"

Jim didn't say anything. He looked around. Mrs. Allen wasn't in the room yet. The kids in the classroom were talking and putting their things away. It was time for class to begin, and still Mrs. Allen hadn't arrived. "Where is Mrs. Allen?" everyone began asking. "Why isn't she here? What's wrong?"

Just then the door opened, and the school principal entered the room, followed by Mrs. Allen. The principal wasn't smiling; neither was Mrs. Allen. Instead, they had serious

expressions on their faces. The students quit talking and turned their attention to the front of the classroom. When everything was quiet, the principal said, "Yesterday, your teacher learned that some students had managed to get a copy of today's history test. We aren't sure yet just how this happened, but we're investigating. Meanwhile, Mrs. Allen has stayed up all night preparing a new test with all new questions. It wasn't easy for her to do so, but she's ready now."

The principal turned and walked out the door, and Mrs. Allen began passing out the test—a completely new test with all new questions.

Some of the students looked puzzled. A few of the students looked sick. But there was joy in Jim's heart. He was happy that he had made the decision to be honest.

Jim picked up the test and began to read the questions. He had studied hard, and he knew he was going to do well.

Think About It!?!

- Would it be all right to cheat on a test if no one ever found out about it?
- Besides the fact that cheating is wrong, can you think of other reasons why cheating is a bad idea?

CHAPTER 25

ROBERT BRUCE AND THE SPIDER

PERSEVERANCE · DETERMINATION

Some seven hundred years ago, the people of Scotland made up their minds that they did not want to be ruled by the king of England. They wanted to rule themselves. This led to war between the two countries.

Again and again, the English army defeated the Scots. At last, Robert Bruce became the leader of the Scottish army. Six times Bruce led his small band of brave men against the much larger forces of England. Six times he was driven back. The last time, his army was scattered, and he had to hide in order to save his life.

Sometimes he hid in the woods. Sometimes he hid in the mountains. And sometimes he hid in the huts of poor peasants. Of course, the English soldiers tried to find and capture him, so Robert had to keep moving from one hiding place to another.

At last he was almost ready to give up. It seemed to him there was no use trying any longer to avoid being captured. That night he lay down on a heap of straw in an old hut. But he couldn't sleep. He was thinking about all his failures. At last, morning came. But as he lay on his bed of straw, he was very discouraged. Would his beloved Scotland ever be free?

Just then Robert saw a small spider trying to swing herself by her thread from one beam of the roof to another. She failed, and the thread swung back to its starting place. She tried again, and again it fell back. She tried the third time, only to fail once more. But this little spider had started out to build a web, and she never thought of giving up. As Robert watched, the spider continued to try to throw the tiny thread across the space between the beams. Six times it fell short.

For a moment, Robert seemed to forget about his own failures. He watched the little spider with deep interest. He hoped she wouldn't give up. He wanted to see her succeed.

The seventh time she swung herself out on her slender line. Would she fail again

as she had the previous six times? No! This time the thread made it across, and the spider quickly fastened it to the beam. Now she had a secure line on which to build her web.

Robert Bruce was ashamed of himself. If a little spider would not give up, why should he? He, too, would try the seventh time. He left his hiding place with new courage. He gathered his friends together. He told them of his plans. He sent them out to encourage his soldiers.

Soon he had rallied another army of brave Scotsmen around him. On June 24, 1314, Robert's small band of Scottish soldiers met the much larger English army in the famous battle of Bannockburn. This time Robert's men completely defeated their enemies. The English soldiers retreated into their own country. Scotland became free, and Robert Bruce became its king.

A tiny spider had shown him the key to success!

Think About It !?!

- Can you really fail as long as you keep trying?
- Why is it that the things that are most important and valuable often require the most effort?

Even the Winds Obey Him

Trust in God

World War I had just ended, but there was still trouble in many places in Europe. Groups of soldiers were making their way toward their homes, and violence was common.

In a certain village lived a good Christian family who loved God and served Him faithfully. One day, soldiers appeared outside the village. More and more soldiers kept coming until they surrounded the town and were camped all around the countryside. They were placed so that they could shoot anyone who tried to leave the village. They demanded food. They took what they wanted, and then they set fire to the town.

The houses in that village all had thatched straw roofs. The weather had been very dry, and a strong wind was blowing. The whole town was rapidly being burned. The flames grew larger and larger as the wind drove the fire straight toward this Christian family's house!

"Father, what shall we do?" the mother and the children asked. "Let's run! Otherwise, we will surely die!"

"If we run out of the house, the soldiers will kill us," the father answered. "I believe God will protect us, for He has promised never to leave us or to forsake us no matter what may come."

Then Father and Mother and the children all knelt down and began to pray. As they prayed, the fire came closer and closer. Before long, the house next to theirs began to burn. The fire came within two feet of their roof. But they kept on praying.

Suddenly, they heard a strange sound. They stopped praying and looked out the windows to see what it was. They saw that the wind had changed and was blowing right away from their house. It was blowing so strongly that the fire could not touch them. God had heard their prayers. They were saved!

"I know there is a God in heaven and that He hears the prayers of His children," the father said. "We are never in danger when the Lord is with us."

Surely, even the winds obey Him.

Think About It

- Does God still perform miracles today?
- Has God ever done something special for you?

TRAPPED IN A TREE!

TRUST IN GOD

"Grandfather, please tell us just one more story," begged Mary while the other children—Joe, Bill, and Janet gathered a little closer. Here is the story Grandfather told.

When I was only ten years old (grandfather began), my mother died, and I was without a home. Some kind people took me to live with them. Later, I went to live with a farmer named Mr. Benson and his wife. One morning, at breakfast, Mr. Benson said to me, "Henry, Mrs. Benson and I have to go into town today. While we're gone, I wish you would go to the woods where we saw those hawks building their nest the other day. Climb up the tree and tear down their nest. The hawks kill our chickens and keep them upset. So, we don't want them to raise more hawks."

After Mr. Benson and his wife drove away in the big wagon, I went into the woods as he had asked me to. I climbed up the tall tree where the hawks were building their nest. There was a place near the top of the tree where a large limb had broken off. That's where the hawks had built their nest. The nest was down in the hollow opening that the branch had left when it broke away.

I clung to the sides of the tree with my hands and put my feet into the opening where the nest was to kick it loose. Suddenly, the nest gave way, and I went tumbling and crashing down, down, down!

When I was able to collect my senses, I was horrified to find that I was inside a hollow tree! I had fallen almost to the ground inside the tree! Try as hard as I could, it was impossible to climb out. I couldn't get any hold on the smooth sides of the trunk. It seemed that I was doomed to die inside that tree.

I began to pray very earnestly to the Lord to save me and help me get out of the tree somehow. All at once, I noticed a little light coming through a small hole in the side of the tree. I could just look out and see a small patch of an old abandoned road. After a while, I was overjoyed to see a team of horses and a wagon coming down the road. When it came near, I began shouting at the top of my voice. The man driving the wagon stopped and turned his head this way and that, listening. He could hear someone shouting, but he couldn't see anyone, and he couldn't make out what I was saying.

I was afraid he would just drive on, so I shouted even louder if that were possible. The man climbed down from the wagon and began walking in my direction. "What are you doing in there?" he asked at last when he found out that the voice was coming from inside the tree.

"I fell down into this tree," I explained through the small hole. "You must get me out. Get an ax and chop me out!"

He went to his wagon and got an ax. Very carefully he chopped a large hole in the side of the tree at the base so that I could crawl out. When he finished he said, "I don't know why I came this way. The horses just seemed to turn down this

old road by themselves. I never come this way. I haven't come down this road in years."

"I know why you did," I told him. "I prayed that the Lord would send someone to help me get out of the tree—and He sent you."

THINK ABOUT IT ?!

- Has God ever helped you when you were in trouble? How?
- Do you think God really hears us when we pray to Him?

WHAT JAMES FOUND IN THE TEAKETTLE

DILIGENCE · RESOURCEFULNESS

A long time ago, in the little village of Greenock, Scotland, there lived a small boy whose name was James. He wasn't a strong boy. Many days he wasn't well enough to go to school and had to stay at home.

James didn't like to run and play and help with work outdoors because the damp, chilly air of Scotland made him shiver. More than anything else he liked to sit in front of the fireplace with his books and read. Or watch the bright red flames curl around the black kettles and go up the chimney. He could sit quietly for hours and hours in front of the fire.

This worried his parents and his aunts and uncles. They said, "James is lazy and doesn't want to work." Now, the Scotch people are hard-working, energetic people, and they have little patience with those who won't work. So, they scolded and scolded James for his laziness. But even if James's hands were idle, his mind was very busy. As he sat in front of the fire, James was thinking about a great many things. He thought and thought.

One day when everyone else was working, James sat as usual by the fireplace. He was carefully watching. And do you know what he was watching so intently? He was watching the teakettle. The kettle was full of water, and as the fire became hotter and hotter, the lid of the kettle sputtered as if it were alive. As James watched, the lid of the kettle moved. *Pop!* It jumped up into the air a little ways and came back down on the kettle with a thump! The cover was heavy too. This made James think and think and think.

He was thinking so hard that he didn't hear his aunt say, "Isn't it a great shame for a boy as big as you to waste his time in front of the fire like that?" She kept on scolding and scolding, but James didn't even hear her.

You see, James wasn't really wasting his time just sitting by the fire. He was thinking. *What is it in the teakettle,* James wondered, *that makes the lid jump up and down like that? Is it alive? Look how strong it is to lift that heavy lid.*

Then James pushed the lid tightly down on the kettle. He held a spoon firmly over the spout of the teakettle. Soon he felt pressure building up against the spoon. It became harder and harder to hold it against the spout, but he held on as tightly as he could. But—*s-s-s-pffft!*—up came the spoon and out came the steam! James couldn't hold the spoon down. The steam was stronger than he was.

That made him think some more. *There is more power in the teakettle than I have in my hands,* he thought. *Why not let the steam do my work for me? They complain because they say I'm lazy, but here is something that can do my work and the work of other people too. If a little steam can have this much power, what could a lot of steam do? Here is a power that can do great things.*

So, James Watt—for that was his name—discovered the power of steam by watching a teakettle heating over the fire. And when James grew up to become a man, he developed an

engine to harness the power of steam. He made improvements on machines that other men had made to use steam power. Today, James Watt is considered to be the "father of the steam engine."

The power that James found in the teakettle was used to power great locomotives that pulled freight trains and passenger cars. James's steam engines drove large ships and powerful machinery in factories. His parents thought James was lazy, but he discovered how to make steam work for him—and others.

Many boys before James had watched teakettles bubble and sing over the fire. But none of them found in the teakettle what James found.

THINK ABOUT IT !?!

- Can a person work just as hard with his brain as someone else does using his muscles?
- What good ideas have you had lately?

THE SHOEMAKER OF HACKLETON

LOVE FOR OTHERS · DILIGENCE

"Willie, we can't send you to school next year," said Mr. Carey. "We have your four brothers and sisters to take care of. And since you're the oldest, you'll have to find a job and go to work. We need the money you can earn."

Now, you may think it would be fun not to have to go to school. But Willie loved school. He loved to study and learn new things. He looked up into his father's face and knew that he had heard right. He would not be able to go back to school the next year! He knew his father wouldn't change his mind.

Willie glanced down at his shoes. He kicked the dust along the path as he and his father walked along. He pretended to be looking for something over by the edge of the trees along the path. He wanted to hide his tears of disappointment. He was so unhappy he couldn't think of anything to say.

"You'll be fourteen years old next week," Father went on. "I think I can get you a job with the shoemaker in town. You can learn to cut leather and make shoes."

"I guess I could study in the evenings," Willie managed to say at last. "There are so many things I want to know! I can borrow books and read and learn things even if I can't go to school."

So, Willie went to work for the town shoemaker, a man named Clarke Nichols, in the town of Hackleton. As soon as he walked into the shoe shop on the very first day, Willie knew that he was going to like his new job. He saw a few books on a shelf in one corner of the shop. Willie could hardly wait to read the titles to see what they were about. He didn't have time to look at them all morning, but when lunchtime came and he could stop work for a few minutes, he quickly began to look at the books.

One of the books looked especially interesting. It was about the Bible. It had a lot of strange words in Greek that Willie didn't understand. But they were exciting anyway. They were like a mysterious puzzle just waiting to be solved.

Willie carefully copied the Greek words on a

piece of paper. He put the paper in his pocket. At the end of the week, when he went home, he took the paper with him. Then he took the paper with the strange Greek words to a friend who could read Greek. With the help of his friend, Willie slowly learned what each word meant. Then he found some Latin words in the book, and he copied these words, as well. He did the same with some Hebrew words. Willie loved to study, and after a few months, he could read Greek, Latin, and Hebrew!

Willie also enjoyed studying his Bible, and he liked to pray. One day he decided he wanted to be a Christian and give

NEPAL
Calcutta

his heart to Jesus. Afterward, he was so happy that he began to tell everyone about Jesus. He wanted to be a preacher, but he had to keep on working making shoes to earn money for food and clothes and to help his family.

One day Willie found a book written by a famous explorer, Captain James Cook, who had traveled to many faraway places around the world. In this book, Willie learned about people who lived in other parts of the world. Then he had an idea.

Willie came to work a few days later carrying a roll of paper under his arm. He got some tacks and a hammer and carefully unrolled the paper. The other workers in the shoe shop came over to see what Willie was doing with the tacks and the roll of paper.

Willie held up the paper so they could see. It was covered with different colored shapes. "This is a map of the world," he told them. "Now we can see what countries Captain Cook visited during his travels."

One of the workmen helped Willie hold up the map against the wall. Willie tacked it in place so all the workers could see it. Then he got a black pencil and began marking the map. He marked each place Captain Cook had been to. He also wrote down things he had learned about each country—things he had learned from books he had read. But while he was writing, he got another idea. He wondered if the people in these faraway places knew anything about Jesus.

"We should send someone across the ocean to teach these people about Jesus," Willie said to his pastor.

"When God wants them to know about Jesus and the Bible, He will take care of it without your help," the pastor told Willie.

But the pastor didn't forget what Willie had said. He talked to other pastors. A few years later there was a movement to send someone to India. "I'll go," Willie offered. "The people in India may not be happy to see me, and my friends here at home may forget about me, but God will be with me." So, Willie sailed for India.

For more than a year after he left for India, no one heard from Willie at all. Finally, a letter arrived. It was from Willie to the pastors who had sent him to India. They read it and passed it around to many other people to read. The letter said that Willie was building a church. He needed help. All his friends began collecting money, which they sent to him to help him build the church in that distant land.

Meanwhile, in India, Willie was having trouble. He didn't know how to speak the Bengali language, so he couldn't talk to the people there. But Willie had always enjoyed learning new things. He decided to get a job so he could have some money to pay someone to teach him Bengali. Willie got a job in a factory making indigo. Indigo is a blue dye that is used to make ink.

As soon as he got a job and began earning some money, Willie hired a teacher. He was a good student, and before long he could speak and understand Bengali. Once he knew the language, Willie started to translate the Bible into Bengali. He knew the people in India would want to read the Bible in their own language. But many of the people couldn't read—even in Bengali. So, Willie held classes to teach them to read. It took a long time, but as the people learned to read and as they began reading the Bible, they wanted to learn more about God.

Willie built a church and a school. He helped many, many people in India to love God and have a better life. From the time he was a boy, Willie had worked hard. He worked hard in the shoemaker's shop. And he worked hard in India as a missionary for God. Today, William Carey is known as the "Father of Modern Christian Missions."

Think About It!?

- Would you enjoy living in a faraway country and learning new customs and languages?
- What is your favorite subject in school? Why?

Saved from the Fire

HELPFULNESS · TRUST IN GOD

Johnny held out his arms to his father. But before he even had a chance to tell his father Goodbye, the soldiers hurried Mr. Wesley away to be locked up in Lincoln Castle.

"Mother," Johnny cried, "why didn't Father pick me up and tell me Goodbye?"

"Your father owes so much money," Mother said, "and we are too poor to pay. The soldiers have to put him in prison until he can pay his debts. It's the law. He wanted to tell you Goodbye, but the soldiers wouldn't let him."

At that time in England people were locked up in jail sometimes when they couldn't pay their debts. And this is what happened to Mr. Wesley. After a while, Johnny's father was released from jail for a while. But as soon as his creditors—the people he owed money to—heard that he was home, they came around demanding that he pay them. They took the cow and the horse. They shouted at Johnny's father.

Mrs. Wesley gathered Johnny and his brothers and sisters around her and tried to comfort them. Before long, someone smelled smoke! Someone else shouted, "Fire! The house is on fire!" Johnny was so excited and so scared that he ran upstairs instead of running outside. There were so many children running in all directions that Mother and Father couldn't keep track of them all. They tried to make sure everyone was safely out of the house, but in all the confusion, they didn't realize that Johnny was missing.

Mother and Father and all the other children were standing in a safe spot underneath a tree in the yard, when all at once they discovered that Johnny wasn't with them!

"I thought you had him," exclaimed Mother to her husband.

"But he's always with you. At least, you always know where he is," Father replied.

Everyone began looking for Johnny. The fire was creeping up to the second-story window. Smoke was pouring from the front door.

"Father! Father!" came a child's faint cry. Mr. Wesley stared into the blazing building. He saw a small hand waving from an upper window.

"Father!" came the voice again. Then Johnny's father saw him. Johnny was standing at the window with the smoke and flames gathering around him! In an instant, Father climbed onto the shoulders of some men standing nearby. They stretched and lifted him as high as they could. Reaching up, Father was able to touch the window. He reached inside, and his strong hands lifted Johnny to safety. He handed the little boy down to his mother. She carried him to the shelter of the big tree where the rest of the family was waiting.

All his life, Johnny was certain that God had saved him from the fire for some important reason. He often wondered what that reason might be. As Johnny grew, his mother taught him about the Bible and Jesus. She taught all her children about God, and it took her a great deal of time to teach all the Wesley children, because there were nineteen of them!

You can imagine that with nineteen children in the family there wasn't much money to go around. But Johnny went to school and decided to become a preacher. He wanted to tell other people about God and His love. Johnny's mother wrote him a letter to encourage him. In the letter, she wrote, "Every morning and evening give your heart to Jesus, and He will save you. Jesus will guide you and give you strength."

Johnny read that letter over and over. Soon he had it memorized. And he prayed every day that Jesus would help him. John Wesley grew up to be a great man of God and a powerful preacher. He learned many lessons from the Bible. He learned that no matter how hard he worked at being good, he could never earn heaven. Heaven is a gift from God that He gives to everyone who believes on Him and loves Him. John Wesley spent his whole life preaching and helping other people know God.

It wasn't always easy for John to preach and teach about God. Sometimes people didn't want to listen. Sometimes people became very angry because they thought John wasn't teaching the Bible correctly. But every time things grew difficult for John, angels would help him.

One winter day, John Wesley was walking to church where he was going to preach. The path went down a steep hill that was covered with ice and snow. It was hard to walk on the path because it was so slippery. As John came down the path a group of angry people crowded against him. They tried to push him to the ground. But John kept walking and hurried on.

One man grabbed John's collar and tried to make him fall. The collar came off in his hand! Then another man came holding a large club. He tried to hit John over the head with it. But just before it struck John's head, it swerved as if pushed aside by an invisible hand. John was sure that an angel had kept the club from hitting him.

Still the angry mob pushed against him. One man raised his fist to hit John. But as he tried to hit him, his arm stopped in midair as if it were frozen. Then gently, he touched John's hair, looking surprised. John knew that an angel had stopped the man's hand.

Finally, John reached the church and began to preach. The mob followed him into the church and started shouting and making fun of him. But as John kept on speaking, they began to listen. Soon they were listening quietly to God's words to their hearts.

Later, John described how God had protected him time and time again. "One man threw a piece of brick and hit my shoulder," he said. "Another struck me with a stone right between the eyes. I've been hit on my way to church and on my way home after the church service. My face has often been bruised and bleeding. Yet I felt no pain because God helped me and I trust Him."

All his life, John tried to help others. He didn't have much money, but sometimes he would go hungry himself to give food to some poor family. John Wesley was always doing kind things for other people—and pointing them to God.

Think About It!?

- When someone does something mean to you, how do you feel? How should you respond?
- Does God have a plan for each person's life? What do you think He is planning for you?

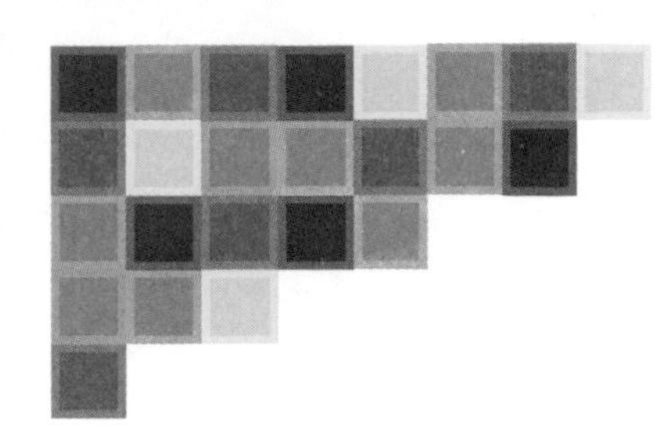

Character-Building Values

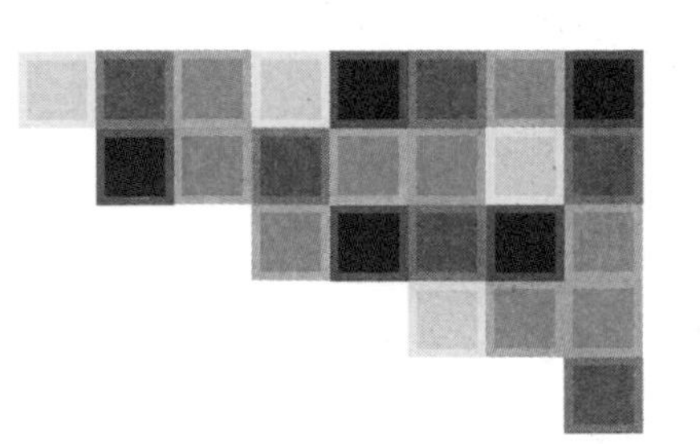

Taught in These Stories

IMAGE CREDITS

p. 5 ©iStockphoto.com / Ira Bachinskaya; p. 6 ©iStockphoto.com / brentmelissa; p. 7 ©iStockphoto.com / Dave Wetzel; p. 9 ©iStockphoto.com / Simone van den Berg; p. 10, 11 ©iStockphoto.com / Timothy Hughes; p. 13 ©iStockphoto.com / Ugur Evirgen; p. 14 ©iStockphoto.com / Leonid Nishko; p. 16, 17 ©iStockphoto.com / Lee; Feldstein; p. 18 ©iStockphoto.com / Martin Lovatt; p. 20 ©iStockphoto.com / kcman02; p. 21 © 2008 Jupiterimages Corporation; p. 22 ©iStockphoto.com / Andrew Johnson; p. 23 ©iStockphoto.com / Alexey Stiop; p. 25 ©iStockphoto.com / Devon Stephens; p. 27 ©iStockphoto.com / Andy Piatt; p. 28, 29 ©iStockphoto.com / Tari Faris; p. 30, 31 ©iStockphoto.com / sarambrosia; p. 32 ©iStockphoto.com / Eric Isselée; p. 35 ©iStockphoto.com / DJM-photo; p. 37 ©iStockphoto.com / Chris Fertnig; p. 38 ©iStockphoto.com / audaxl; p. 39 ©iStockphoto.com / Lai Leng Yiap; p. 40 ©iStockphoto.com / blackie; p. 42, 43 ©iStockphoto.com / Peter Wey; p. 45 ©iStockphoto.com / Nicholas Homrich; p. 46 ©iStockphoto.com / (chips) Ever, (trail mix) Bridgette Braley, (pie) Greg Ferguson; p. 47 ©iStockphoto.com / Jack Puccio; p. 48 ©iStockphoto.com / JoLin; p. 49 ©iStockphoto.com / Kameleon007; p. 50–53 Michelle C. Petz; p. 53 ©iStockphoto.com / (cat) Tina Rencelj; p. 54 ©iStockphoto.com / Yong Kian Lim; p. 55 ©iStockphoto.com / Todd Bates; p. 56 ©iStockphoto.com / stocksnapper; p. 57 ©iStockphoto.com / Jim Lopes; p. 58 ©iStockphoto.com / Wellford Tiller; p. 59 ©iStockphoto.com / Joseph C. Justice Jr.; p. 61 ©iStockphoto.com / George Clerk; p. 62 ©iStockphoto.com / Jonathan Brizendine; p. 63 ©iStockphoto.com / Darryl Sleath; p. 64, 65 ©iStockphoto.com / George Argyropoulos; p. 67 ©iStockphoto.com / Kristian Sekulic; p. 68, 69 ©iStockphoto.com / DavidGarry; p. 70 ©iStockphoto.com / Jill Fromer; p. 71 ©iStockphoto.com / (dollar) blackred, (dime) pomortzeff; p. 73 ©iStockphoto.com / Jani Bryson; p. 75 ©iStockphoto.com / Shannon Long; p. 76 ©iStockphoto.com / Millanovic; p. 78 ©iStockphoto.com / John Butterfield; p. 79 ©iStockphoto.com / Shane Stezelberger; p. 80, 81 ©iStockphoto.com / Selahattin Bayram; p. 83 ©iStockphoto.com / Todor Marholev; p. 85 ©iStockphoto.com / Rick Lord; p. 86 ©iStockphoto.com / Michael Zwahlen; p. 87 ©iStockphoto.com / Daniel Kourey; p. 88 ©iStockphoto.com / (magnifying glass) Mustafa Deliormanli, (india map) Marisa Allegra Williams; p. 91 ©iStockphoto.com / Dan Brandenburg; p. 92 ©iStockphoto.com / Sean Locke